VOICES BEYOND THE BORDER

BORDER

Living with
Borderline Personality Disorder

edited by

LUCY ROBINSON
&
VICKY COX

G000299440

supporting personality disorder

Selection, introduction and notes
copyright © 2005 Borderline UK Ltd.

Copyright of poems and prose rests with the individual
authors.

ISBN: 1904697836

First published 2006 by
Chipmunkapublishing
PO Box 6872
Brentwood
Essex CM13 1ZT
United Kingdom

All rights reserved. No part of this book may be
reproduced, stored in a retrieval system, or transmitted
in any form, or by any means, electronic, mechanical,
photocopying, recording or otherwise, without prior
written permission of the copyright holders.

Chipmunkapublishing only controls the publication rights
to this publication and does not control the rights to the
poems and prose in this anthology.

www.chipmunkapublishing.com

Dedicated to the memory of

KAY SHAFER

&

ALL OF THOSE
FOR WHOM
THE NIGHTS WERE TOO LONG

CONTENTS

6

3 RECOVERY AND BEYOND

4 THOSE AROUND US

5 RESOURCES

This book was conceived as the result of an unlikely match between an eminent, august and traditional organisation, and a modern, emergent and edgy one. Without wanting to gender stereotype, the former provided the money to make it possible - while the latter created, nurtured and cared for it until it emerged into the world. Thanks to Oxford Postgraduate Medical and Dental Education Department and its recent "Patients Teaching Doctors" grant and to Borderline UK for its inspired, energetic and committed membership. Thanks also to The Health Foundation, who supported my participation in this and other projects with BUK and service users in the emerging field of "personality disorder".

Personality Disorder is a ghastly term for a very common disposition: the very juxtaposition of words reveals its authoritarian subtext. It suggests that "these people" are not like us; their characters are flawed and there is probably very little that can be done about "it". This is clearly nonsense: 1 in 20 people cannot be written off as faulty human beings, suffer great distress and anguish, and yet be undeserving of suitable mental health services.

The consultation exercise with service users for formulation of Government policy revealed the passion and depth of feeling about this. Many eloquently described how they had been treated as less than human by, for example, psychiatric ward staff, A&E doctors and GPs. The civil servants drafting the policy suddenly sat up and listened: here was a large health need that was going completely unmet. The Government was suddenly hearing the voice of service users themselves, not professionals arguing for more staff, or services, or research. It was clear that a multitude of people are suffering severely disabling alienation and social exclusion, often without any hope of help, and sometimes being made worse by those there to help. About one in eight people diagnosed "borderline" kill themselves.

Yet the public perception is like the diagnostic label - of frightening, dangerous people who inhabit a different world to "our" own. The truth is that those to whom the label could apply are far more likely to be frightened by everybody else, and a danger to themselves. But risk to the public trumps any more humane considerations, so the few dozen "dangerous people with severe personality disorder" are treated in facilities costing over £100m per year, while all those who suffer in silent desperation received nothing until 2004, and then about £20m per year for more than two million people. That's about £100,000 per head if you endanger other people in your suffering, and about £10 per head if you are deemed only a risk to yourself.

Hopefully this book will help to let this nasty clinical secret out into the light. Perhaps it will be like the dreaded and unmentionable "cancer" word a couple of generations ago, shameful, untreatable, unspeakable and nearly always terminal – but now openly discussed in the media, understood ever better by public and professionals, and often completely cured. Borderline UK has started this: people do not *have* a "personality disorder", rather they are "borderline persons", rightly proud of many aspects of their personalities, and willing to speak out about it. More widely, when humane and effective treatments are provided for those diagnosable with personality disorder, many more people will be able to talk about it, not need to feel ashamed, and help each other with it. I hope that the contributions in this book will be an encouragement to that enlightenment – to provide a window of understanding for those whose lives are not like this, and a statement of comradeship for those who are.

Dr Rex Haigh MRCPsych
Personality Disorder Development Consultant
National Institute for Mental Health in England –
South East Development Centre

Introduction

In the UK today approximately 1.6 million people awoke to the same problem (that's if they'd managed to sleep) – how to survive another day alongside the torrid and turbulent emotions associated with Borderline Personality Disorder (BPD). Although you'd struggle to find a room big enough to house them all at once, it's not a 'popular' mental health problem and it receives little publicity. The fact that you've heard of it at all probably means you have it or somebody very close at hand does. In the immense isolating pain and confusion BPD can bring with it, this book is here to remind you that you are not alone – there are *at least* 1,599,999 others who feel their own personal version of your suffering. This unique anthology brings you some of their voices.

In 2000 a small band of people in the UK who had been diagnosed with BPD settled their disillusionment with the frustrating lack of information about the disorder and established Borderline UK (BUK). This was the first organisation dedicated to BPD and run predominantly by service users themselves. The aim was to fill a large and growing gap in information and support for individuals with this controversial diagnosis. Even the concept that gave it such a confusing name – that 'borderline' describes a set of people who lie on the border of a psychotic illness – is no longer held to be true. The characteristic emotional instability, uncertainty of self, and displays of dramatic or dangerous behaviour BPD engenders have been obstructive for many in their ongoing search for help. In 2002 the UK government pronounced that personality disorder should no longer be a 'diagnosis of exclusion' in an effort to prevent mental health service providers turning away patients on the basis of their diagnosis. Borderline UK has been fully supportive of these efforts and has engaged extensively in consultancy work to pull personality disorder higher up the agenda.

This book grew out of that and other supportive ventures BUK has established or been involved with. Being diagnosed with BPD – for those who are told about it – brings a strange mix of emotions. In the public mind the phrase 'personality disorder' rings alarm bells of danger and violence, and current levels of education and awareness do little to dispel this myth – people with BPD are far more likely to harm themselves than anybody else. The phrase is a way of dividing 'us' from 'them' and writing off the cause of emotional distress as an internal character flaw. Many people with BPD find a good way to deal with this social isolation is to hear from other people who have the diagnosis. Bearing that in mind, the hard-working volunteers at ·BUK decided to make sharing the experience that little bit easier by writing to all of BUK's members and anyone else we could think of who might be willing and able to share their thoughts and feelings. The result is a truly unique account of life with BPD told by many different voices from many different angles. This book won't teach you facts and figures about BPD or the latest theories as to what causes or treats it, but it will provide the aspect of BPD that is almost always missed – how it *feels*.

However, BPD is not the sort of disorder that only affects the person diagnosed with it. Carers and service providers also struggle to make sense of the behaviour of individuals diagnosed with BPD. We decided that any book omitting this aspect would be one chapter too short and so rallied around those carers and mental health professionals who were willing to air their views.

After months of work and setting, then re-setting deadlines, Voices Beyond the Border finally took shape. The book is divided up into several chapters and begins at the beginning – with diagnosis. Receiving a diagnosis of BPD was a relief for some, like having some sort of answer, or a piece of the puzzle solved. For others it was confusing, daunting and spelled the end of hope. As diagnosis so often comes along with treatment, the next section includes people's many and varied experiences of the mental health system. The following chapter contains people's experiences of everyday life with BPD – all the different emotions, behaviours, and consequences it carries. When the contributions were received, they didn't map neatly onto the nine diagnostic criteria commonly used for diagnosis (see appendix), so they were classified according to the most frequently encountered experiences. It's a reflection on the complexity of BPD that the 'miscellaneous' section is so large! Chapter three has pieces reflecting on the most contentious issue of all – recovery from BPD. Whilst it's said that a personality disorder is for life, not just for adolescence, recovery **is** possible. This chapter contains confirmation that there is hope – there is somewhere beyond the border. The voices of carers and mental health professionals can be heard in chapter four, with some frank admissions and deeply personal experiences.

Please be warned that it is not always easy reading. We haven't stolen or quietened anybody's voice, although the names appearing within pieces have been changed. Whilst there are no graphic descriptions of acts of self-harm, there are allusions to it and a few swear words if you know where to look. Please, if you are feeling vulnerable or unsafe do not read those sections. This book is here to provide empathy rather than become another weapon in the armament. If you do find yourself feeling upset or simply wishing to seek out more information or support, visit one of the websites or contact one of the organisations listed in the resources section.

All that remains to say is thanks to all the people whose hard work and dedication have transformed this madly sketched idea into a reality. Massive thanks to Dr Rex Haigh and the Oxford Postgraduate Medical and Dental Education Department, who provided the funding to send this book to press. Thanks also to everyone who gave their time – completely voluntarily – to help. Thank you to Jason Pegler at Chipmunka Publishing for enabling us to see this in print and for helping us along the journey.

The biggest thanks must go to the people who sent and e-mailed us their poetry and prose. Some have felt able to provide their real names, whereas others have preferred to remain anonymous while BPD remains such a stigmatised diagnosis. The willingness to share their personal experiences in order to help others has made this book the special addition to the literature on BPD that it is. For now though, simply sit back and begin your journey beyond the border...

Vicky Cox and Lucy Robinson
Editors

1. EXPERIENCE OF DIAGNOSIS AND TREATMENT

Diagnosis

Labels – The Most Stigmatised Diagnosis – BPD
Naomi Salisbury

It got me out of hospital, it got me fighting back, it found me some of the most caring and amazing people I've ever come across. Which was not quite what I expected. I didn't intend to spend the hottest summer in ages stuck in a boiling hot hospital where you couldn't even open the windows, getting some of the weirdest and most alarming news of my life. Being given a diagnosis that at first I didn't understand suddenly made a lot of things make sense. I think the consultant was trying to cheer me up when he told me the worst years are the 20s and 30s (I'm 24!). But some of the most important things I learned weren't the specifics of the diagnosis. It was more that an illness shouldn't define who you are, and a label shouldn't condemn you. The girl I shared a room with asked me – are you borderline? – and even as I was answering yes I was realising that's only one way to look at it and it's not the way I choose. Your diagnosis might help you understand the way you're living, but it doesn't mean you have to live it out. Labels are in the end only words.

The people I have met since who have BPD are some of the kindest, most caring and understanding people I have ever met. The support we're able to give each other is amazing. I read once that you can tell someone with BPD almost anything as the chances are they will have done it or know someone who has!

At first I was glad to have an explanation for my weird behaviour, then I was determined not to be defined by a label. Now I'm just glad to know that there are people out there who will listen to me rant and that I can do the same for them. Even if we have a hard time believing it about ourselves, every day we prove to each other that we are all much more than a label.

To learn how to live is the biggest challenge of all.

Untitled
Ruth

I was diagnosed borderline personality disorder three and a half years ago – the main reason being my self-harm and past anorexia. I felt that the psychiatrist should have seen me more than once before making this diagnosis. I found out by guesswork – discovering through an internet search that a senior house officer I was seeing was on a course about treating people with severe personality disorders and was using me as a case study.

A Study in Blue
Anonymous

I was given the diagnosis of Borderline Personality Disorder in May 2001, a week before my 28th birthday, by highly respected clinicians working from a psychotherapy department with a purported speciality in diagnosis and treatment of individuals with BPD. By way of an explanation, I was given a copy of the ICD-10 and DSM-IV criteria and a photocopy of "Walking on Eggshells". I left the office confused, scared and perhaps a little relieved. I knew nothing about personality disorders at this point, borderline or otherwise, and in my naïvety thought it was something professionals would be falling over themselves to help me with!

Until the reality dawned on me; that there really was very little support, understanding or compassion for this condition. In fact it gave the green flag to the professionals who were involved to withdraw their support from here on in. So I found myself alone trying to deal with this thing, whatever it was.

As no help or information was forthcoming, I turned to the Internet for advice, which was a medium I was not familiar with and rather suspicious of. I read report after report about the "problems" that borderlines pose in treatment and how healthcare providers should "deal with" borderlines. I read much about those diagnosed with a PD finding themselves at the mercy of the criminal system and I started to wonder if there were actually any "ordinary" people, like me. The same words kept jumping out at me; manipulative, deceitful, attention seeking, shallow, exaggerating, impulsive; the list went on. I wasn't **those** things! *Was I?*

Searches resulted in any number of news groups and discussion forums in the seemingly forward thinking US, but I could find no actual help anywhere closer to home, in the UK. I became more and more disheartened as I realised that this was a label to be ashamed of, something which would pigeon hole me and make people wary or scared of me. The only remotely local organisation which had personality disorders on its agenda appeared to focus on those who had committed offences, but in the absence of anything more appropriate, I contacted them. They really couldn't offer any practical help but gave me the details of someone setting up a support network in Cumbria.

Borderline UK was but a fledgling at that time, just a few resolute members – but I was made to feel at home and accepted. As I wasn't sure of myself, I was happy just to "listen" to other people's conversations. Their experiences were comforting, saddening and maddening as they related their accounts of life, work, relationships, traumas and disillusionment with the National Health Service. But there was humour, good times and personal triumphs. And for the most part I felt I was somewhere that understood.

Unlike my life away from the computer, where I felt increasingly maligned and alienated. Rather than empowering me, I felt my voice had been taken away and I had nowhere to turn. My partner of many years was also taking the position that much of my behaviour could be ascribed to BPD and I felt I couldn't argue with that – after all *I* was the one who had been diagnosed as having a flawed personality, so I had no ammunition with which to retaliate. I made several attempts to return to the job I loved and each time I failed after only a few months.

Over the years, I have felt increasingly unable to cope and have asked many times for help, and many times been turned away. My partner and I have had some pretty bloody battles with the services and all to no avail. My mood was lowering and darkening until I got to a point where I knew I needed help, but I also knew by now that this label of BPD meant I couldn't have that help. Everything was hopeless, pointless and futile – I was a burden to friends, family and colleagues. I could see no way out.

Which brings me more or less up to date; after a failed suicide attempt last year I am slowly trying to rebuild my life, desperately trying to repair relationships and friendships, salvage my career. Only now, I have an ally in the shape of a new psychiatrist who has seen me without prejudice and given me the time and space to talk. He believes, in this instance at least, that there has been a misdiagnosis and asserted, quite simply, that I do not have BPD and probably never did. The next challenge is the complex process of overturning the original diagnosis

Which is great news. Or is it? It really doesn't actually change a thing: I'm still me, with the same problems as before. Only maybe now I'll start getting the help I have needed all along. Not that I, or countless others, didn't need it then, it's just that we haven't been wearing the right label. It's taking some time to come out of the shadows, sure as I am that nothing will have changed.

I understand and accept some of the hypotheses of how a borderline personality may evolve; I can see the processes and effects in myself. But it's that particular combination of personality traits, some lovable, some loathsome, that makes me who I am, and all of us simply unique individuals. If you can show me a person who doesn't have some defect or flaw in their personalities, I'll show you a person with no personality at all!

Many of the borderlines I have met in the past few years have shown me the best aspects of the human character; they are amongst the wittiest, brightest, most caring and determined people I have ever known. Their friendships I value and my life has been enriched by simply knowing them.

Untitled
Mark Oliver

In my experience as a staff nurse working in acute psychiatric wards, I've lost count of the number of times I've talked to people who have just been given a diagnosis of BPD and they've gone and done a bit of research and been desperately unhappy at what they've found. "I have a problem with my personality and reading about it, it sounds dreadful!" It's human nature to want to be told exactly what's wrong with you, but the reality of being given a diagnosis somehow seems to make things worse. You go from a person with a unique mix of experiences and problems and become a person who is summed up by a phrase – and what an ugly phrase – "personality disorder."

Well, if I were you, I wouldn't pay too much attention to the diagnosis – it's just a bunch of words, a phrase, at the end of the day. It could just as easily be called something else, and if it did it mightn't sound so bad, "I've examined you and you've got Pointer's Syndrome, or "Leaf's Syndrome", or whatever. It's just a phrase. It doesn't say anything about *you* as a *person*. The other thing about a diagnosis is that it's a label, and labels tend to distort how people see themselves and how they are seen by other people. They're not terribly helpful when it comes to seeing people as individuals. But here's a secret about diagnosing – it's a *guess!* It's usually a pretty good guess, but it's what doctors do when they are faced with a collection of symptoms – they look at them and have a good guess as to what medical disorder they most resemble. It's why people sometimes want second opinions or why they might be given more than one diagnosis. It's particularly difficult in the field of psychiatry because certain symptoms can be found in different disorders. I'm not putting doctors down – I think they do a great job – but don't get too hung up about diagnosis.

Identity Crisis
Ashman

I'm a waller, a signer,
A web page designer,
A writer, a poet,
(Though you'd never know it);
A singer, a thinker,
A compulsive drinker,
A visionary dreamer,
An impotent schemer;
A rebel, a smoker,
A first rate no-hoper,
A petal, a flower,
An orgasmic hour;
A ghost on the border,
A threat to your order
A thorn in your pride,
A motorbike ride;
A weight on your mind,
Truly one of a kind,
A deserted ship,
Your very worst trip;
Your greatest mistake,
An arrogant fake,
A knock on the door,
An obsessive bore,
A shadow of me
Labelled Bee Pee Dee.

Please Don't Judge
Anonymous

It's not the bpd itself that bothers me so much as all
the attitudes from other people and what it has

26

caused and all that jazz. And that causes more to deal with and it's hard..... seems like it's a label so people then think you are just like the criteria for diagnosis all the time and won't give you any credit for how well you do the rest of the time.

The Relief of Diagnosis
Judith M. Galloway

For as long as I can consciously remember I have had problems negotiating "normality". Even as a very young child, my peers perceived me as somehow different, which led to periods of being completely ostracised, mixed with temporary, intense and highly unstable friendships. I was bullied a lot, and taken advantage of a lot. Year by year, the situation failed to improve as I dragged myself through one misery, one disappointment, one agony after another. I reached my teens and became what is now referred to as a "school refuser". I started to self-harm, and I made two or three half-hearted and spectacularly unsuccessful suicide bids – which I can now honestly say were confused, desperate cries for help. In the early 1980s, the educational psychologist removed me to a special school.

My adult life reflected the same sort of patterns – intense relationships, full of manipulation (mine) and distrust (mine) that inevitably failed, jobs that came and went, goals that were half-reached. Confusion and chaos. I settled into an endlessly repeating cycle of reasonable times, when I functioned well enough to socialise and go to work, followed by set backs which I perceived as utter catastrophes – redundancy, deaths of relationships, burglary, accidents. I drifted in and out of the auspices of GPs and specialists, was treated for stress, depression, headaches. I was tested for epilepsy, but there were never any answers. I saw counsellors, I over-analysed myself, I searched endlessly for reasons why I was the way I was. Surely, if I could not cope with everyday life the way other people coped, then I must be some kind of inadequate freak?

I finally got married – a high point! I then lost my job, had a serious car accident and moved 200 miles from friends and family – low points. Eventually, in the jurisdiction of a new health authority, the cycle of my life repeated, I started to self-harm, to suffer panic attacks and dissociation, to hear voices and to rage continuously and pointlessly. My GP prescribed anti-depressants (which had helped before), and referred me to the mental health team. All very old ground to me, ·except...

In 2004, at the age of 37, I met a psychiatrist who seemed to be genuinely listening to what I had to say. I told him about my anger, my self-hate, my fear, and my inability to deal consistently with life's little ups and downs. I told him about the things in my childhood I haven't discussed here. It was a very, very long session. As we neared the end of the marathon, he wrote some things down for me and told me to go away and research them (I'm good at research!). There were medications he wanted me to look at, and the words "Emotionally Unstable Personality Disorder: Borderline Type". I'd never heard of such a thing.

My husband and I went away and did as we'd been instructed. We scoured the Internet, bought the books. It didn't take us very long to agree that the person all the books and articles were talking about was me! The DSM-IV Definition was an almost one hundred percent accurate description of who and what I was. I was... stunned. Amazed. Suddenly, there was me, my life, written in black and white before us.

We went back to the psychiatrist for confirmation. In his opinion the diagnosis stood: I was a Borderline!

Nothing can describe the utter relief I felt (and still feel) to have a diagnosis. I felt validated, vindicated. Finally, there was a "reason" for everything...

For me, a diagnosis has helped make sense of the utter chaos of my life to date. It has helped me understand who I am, and why I react as I do. It has been a huge and important step on the long, long road to recovery. Of course, I understand that having a diagnosis is not a magic wand or an excuse – it is not a panacea. However, for me it is a stable point in an unstable world. I am not mad, I am not bad. I am Borderline. The label does not define me as a person, but it helps me to a new comprehension.

I have scars on my arms and scars on my psyche. Some days I beat my head with my fists. I scream and rage and cry. Everything hurts far, far too much... but...

...I have a good marriage (better than I deserve?!), a home of my own, and a CV that includes some "good" past jobs. I have both an Open University Diploma in Social Policy and Criminology and a Bachelor of Science degree, which I worked hard for during some incredibly tough times.

I still suffer, but I no longer suffer alone and in ignorance. I know what and why, and I know I am not the only one – and to me that is immensely important. I do not believe that the relief diagnosis can bring can be over-estimated. For me, at least, it has been a blessing, not a curse.

So... why am I Borderline? I guess that's another story... I wonder if it has a happy ending?

Treatment

Psychodynamically Challenged
Ashman

Tight-lipped and Gothic
Her face set
And professionally styled
By a half-smiling Bhudda,
She nods in all the right places
And offers to me
Appropriate faces:
Red meat with red wine,
White wine with fish.

Trouble At T'Supermarket
Ashman

A supermarket trolley's
Not the best of things to lean on
When you're reeling from the questions
That your therapist's just asked:
Why d'ya think.....?
And *What d'ya feel...?*
And *Where the fuck's the beans?*
Did you ever think to shop would be a Herculean
task?

31

Beyond the Horizon
Mick Burke

If "even a journey of a thousand miles,
Must begin with a single step,"
The only advantage,
Confucious I say,
Is that at walking you'll become adept.
I jest of course, this fabled saying,
Not to be taken literally,
But at your lowest point,
It lends itself,
To sarcasm and irony.

Back Again
Celia

Back again
But for what purpose?
More stilted conversation
More meaningless words.

Out of the window
Dark, dreary houses
Inside middle-class and punk
Sit, patiently side by side.

But why is she here
This middle-class housewife?
No physical illness
Just empty pain……deep inside.

What can they give her
More pills or a chat?
But for what purpose

There is no miracle cure.

A picture in her pocket
Three kings and a star
Drawn by her son
Close yet so far.

Perhaps she should leave
Slip silently away.
No, she sits longer
There's nowhere to go.

Untitled
Ruth

I depend on services now for someone to tell me I am doing well. To compliment me and recognise my achievements - seeing me as more than a self harmer and someone with BPD.

The visit from my community psychiatric nurse brings me back to normality. I move away from my pain, the gnawing emptiness. I engage in normal conversation. My feelings are acknowledged. I become less afraid of the void while she is here and start to face it. But I can only do this a bit at a time and it is a long process. I need to meet new people who will distract me from the emptiness and help fill it with new stimuli. I want to feel that I do not need to cut or starve to deserve attention – justifying the help I receive from others.

Along with the desire to be noticed is a painful shyness. I prefer my own company most of the time but pay for it. I want to be with others but on my own terms. It makes the way forward difficult. But I feel the emptiness will engulf me if I do not take steps to counter it.

I hate the term attention seeking. It is easy for services to label us with this. I have learnt through the psychodynamic work with my CPN that wanting an emotional attachment is normal. It is something we all need. That makes myself and others with BPD more balanced than the way we are perceived.

Dianne's Medical Records

Dianne Aslett

Dr.Stanley, po-faced, superior
Truly, he's scared, and when
upon his posterior
firmly clasped hands rest and intend
to feign coolness
as we march to his den -
they don't fool me.

Dr. Davies, scruffy and skinny,
his clothes hang off him
like sloughing a snake skin
his body writhes inside,
a lobotomy he'd like to order me
- or anything that'd make his life easy.
He pretends to be
in control, cheerful, mean well,
but truly he's out of his depth.
Hostile and hateful, as depressed as hell
and probably will commit suicide
before I do.

34

Arnold, flustered, disorganized,
fusses over me confusedly, remains
contracted in, constrained and
knuckled-well-under by
the Establishment he espouses
so solidly.
Arnold apologizes profusely,
embarrassed as I cry
as if it's his fault.
Ever forgetful, frustrated,
breathlessly
he expresses the wish to be
contracted-out, and really,
that's okay by me.
Anyway, I think, Arnold retires in May.

Dr. Johnson (Steve) kind and close
his correctness, professionalism
binding me
in welcome structure, oozes
sensitivity, protects me,
cares and comprehends
- stands up for me, my fantasy supposes,
I don't really know: it's what I hope for though.

Anyway, of them all
I like best Dr. Steve Johnson.

He's really cool.

In Memoriam
Ashman

"This is a war we're fighting here,"
Said my fragile and frightened friend,
"And they're killing us, one by lonely one
With their anti-psychotics, their sedatives,
Their anti-depressants and tranquilisers;
With their chemical medications,
Criminalisations
And professionally required procrastinations;
With their dog-died looks, Habitat sympathy,
And outrageous lack of empathy;
With their smug "we know best" attitudes,
Philosophy and platitudes,
Labels, badges and pigeon holes,
Life-long comments on medical records,
And the inhumanity of Section 3."

"This is a war we're fighting here,"
Said my fragile and frightened friend.
Well, all wars have fatalities --
And you became one, last weekend.

You Say, I Hear: *A Guide to a No-Win Situation*
Anonymous

You say: I'll see you in six weeks
I hear: You don't care. You think I'm faking it. If you
thought I was *really* ill, you'd want to see me
sooner.

You say: You look better than last time I saw you.

I hear: You think I'm fine, you don't believe me when I tell you I'm struggling. You're going to discharge me and leave me with no help.

You say: nothing

I hear: You don't want to hear how I'm feeling. I want to tell you that I've been cutting and that these new tablets make me feel nauseous, but as you're not asking you must not want to know.

You say: How's your appetite been?

I hear: You think I've put on weight.

You say: Well, I can see things are difficult at the moment, but I'm not sure you'd benefit from hospitalisation.

I hear: You want me dead. You don't care. You think I'm faking it. You'll be sorry when I'm dead.

You say: Do you think going into hospital might be a good idea?

I hear: Finally, someone sees how bad things are. Thank you. Now everyone will believe me. Mum will be sorry for hassling me. I can have a break.

You say: Do you think going into hospital might be a good idea?

I hear: That's the last thing I want, what are you thinking? It'll make me worse. I can't tell you the truth anymore.

You say: I'd like to increase your medication.
I think: YES!!!! I must be properly ill to merit that. I have a reason for feeling so awful.

You say: I'd like to increase your medication.
I think: FUCK. I don't want to be on more tablets. They make me sluggish and flat. I hate them.

A Story from My Life: *Finding a voice*
Gail Silver

The door opens.
A head pops round.
It withdraws.
The door closes.

I don't exist.
I am not here.
I'm being ignored.
Rejected.
Abandoned.

The story of my life!

The door opens.
"Just doing the checks."
The door closes.

Nobody knocks.
My space is invaded.
I'm not worthy of respect.
I'm not important.
Nobody cares.

The story of my life!

The door opens.
"Are you OK?"
The door closes.

Still nobody knocks.
Nobody waits for an answer.
My heart cries out, *'Don't leave!'*
My mind shouts, *'I'm not OK!'*
My body says, *'I'm in such pain!'*
Nobody wants to hear me.

The story of my life!

Somebody knocks.
I say nothing.
Somebody looks in.
"Hello Gail. How are you?"
I say nothing.
The door closes.

I can't look.
I can't speak.
I don't know what to say.
I won't know how to say it.
I curl into a tighter ball.

The story of my life!

Why can't you stay with me?
Why can't you talk to me?

Why can't you hold me?
Why can't you take this pain away?
Why don't you make me better?
Why won't it stop?

I want to die!

The story of my life!

Oh! The pain!
Oh the agony,
The confusion!
Which way do I go?
What shall I do?
Where can I hide?
WHY is nobody there?

The anger, the rage!
The fury, the turmoil!
The loneliness. Such isolation!
Where are you?
Why have you abandoned me?
WHY IS NOBODY THERE?

I WANT TO DIE!

THE STORY OF MY LIFE!!

Someone knocks.
The door opens.
Someone says, "Can I come in?"
I nod my head slowly.
The someone comes in, closes the door
And sits by my bed.
I'm still facing the wall,

Still curled – like a baby growing –
Waiting to be born.
Someone. The person, says quietly,
"Gail, look at me."
I can't.
"Gail, look at me."
I can't.
"Gail, I can't help you if you won't talk to me,"
The person says softly.
I turn over and face Helen.
I burst into tears.
She takes hold of my hand
And stays with me for a while
As I cry.
Oh, such tears and heart-rending sobs!
Such pain floods out and a few words too.
A new beginning for my life.

I can go through the door.
I talk to Helen.
I am learning that
Some people can be trusted.
Some people are there for me.
I am learning
To say how I feel,
To ask for help.
I know now that I can change,
But I need help to do it.
I am learning so many, many things.
More changes in my life.

Someone knocks at the door.
I say, "Come in!"
The door opens.

Helen comes in.
"How are you?" she asks.
"Much better thank you.
"I'm going home today!"
"I'm pleased." "So am I."
"Good Luck!" " Thank you!"

The door opens.
I go out.
The door closes.

I am at another new beginning.
A journey of self discovery.
Learning to change how I think.
Learning how to manage moods.
Learning how to manage anger.
Learning how to manage anxiety.
It will take a long time.
It will be hard and painful.
·But I shall do it.
I have help.

From today I am here.
I do exist.
I am not always ignored,
Or rejected and abandoned.
Many things will change too....

The story of my life.

Two O/D's

Mary-Anne Sloan

What are they trying to do to me?

This is malice; pure, evil malice, deliberately trying to foul things up for me. I can only imagine that the medical profession is deliberately trying to drive me to suicide. I lose it, slam the phone down, sit and sob for a while, and make the only decision open to me. Well, not the only one; I won't destroy myself yet, because then they'd have won – but if they won't listen to words, I'll have to see if they'll listen to something else. And I'm calm, very very calm, because at last I've made a decision, at last there's something I can do. You have to offer something, of course. Either really offer your life, or at least take a chance. I have gambled my liver against the hope that someone will listen.

Calmly to the phone and to the front door to wait and here is an ambulance, and I feel so stupid and hopeless, stupid to have to waste people's time because no-one would listen to me, stupid that I couldn't find any other way, and I sob and sorry my way to the hospital, suddenly contrite.

Feeling very guilty now, guilty for the kind cheerful nurses who don't judge me when they should, they above all have the right to judge. Not too keen on the doctor, though, she seems to have the attitude problem so prevalent in her profession, but perhaps that's just the sickness talking...

The night has gone and I'm very guilty and contrite now, and very dopey and out of it, so it's a good time for a psychiatrist to come round. Not a good start – he drapes his Pierre Cardin coat (I kid you not) over my drip stand, and I know that this one has more than the usual deficiencies of his worthless profession. The only thing he gives a shit about is when he thinks I'm going to be sick on his coat (and how I wish I had been).

And so it goes. But now I am starting to feel less ill and the terror and hopelessness return in all their horror and I sob to any passing nurse and feel hopeless and know more despair than ever I have known even in my sad and useless life...

Never mind, now it's Friday and I'm in the van on the way to Glasgow, very worried about it all, and with good reason, for now the van's become an ambulance and I'm on the way to Casualty again, contrite again, ashamed again, wondering why again. Why? Why did I do it? Why? It was a good day. I got upset, got upset because someone pointedly refused to hold my hand at one of the final dances. And I still don't know why, why this trivial incident pushed me over the edge, but it did.

It's comforting being here again. No-one can hurt me here. No-one can get at me. No-one even knows that I'm here. It's glorious sunshine outside, but I prowl around on my own, occasionally being nasty to nurses, not really knowing why I feel what I feel or what has happened to me. I have suffered a mental catastrophe without knowing it, and I doubt if I'll ever really understand...

After a while the doctor wants to discharge me. He's saying I can't stay in forever. 'Wish I could', says my diary...

Psychiatrists Are Not All Idiots
And pssst.... Sometimes they actually know what's best.

Anonymous

A means of bonding amongst services users seems to be moaning about their care team. I've always believed that you can tell how far along someone is in recovery by how much they slag off their psychiatrist, CPN et al. The angry newly diagnosed borderline spends a significant amount of time ranting, feeling mistreated, misunderstood and maligned.

I was no different.

Part One

My first experience of a psychiatrist was in a ward round following my first admission to a psychiatric ward. This man had never set eyes on me, his underlings had prescribed me mind-numbing concoctions of anti-psychotics and anti-depressants. He took one look at me and said: 'you don't need to be here, you should go home today.'

I flipped out. How could this man that didn't know me send me home based on a first-impression assessment? How could someone so trained not realise that I am the definition of apparent competence and that underneath my cheerful exterior, I was planning my death? How could he send me home when he knew I had nowhere to go? I ran round the ward in typical borderline fashion, telling anyone who would listen how awful this psychiatrist was, how much he hated me, how I was going to overdose as soon as I got home and *then* he'd be sorry. And I was amazed when this behaviour didn't gain me another week's respite.

A few years later, I was reflecting on this admission and was surprised to realise that this psychiatrist, this man who my life only crossed with for five minutes, had done me right. He'd seen that although I'd ended up in an inpatient unit, I didn't have the makings of a career psychiatric patient and pushed me out before I could be tempted to get on that path. He'd seen that, through conversations with other patients, I was dangerously expanding my knowledge of self harm and purging techniques and that since my admission, the frequency and severity of my self-harm had increased ten-fold. He'd seen that I was taking on too many of the problems of other patients to my own detriment. He had the foresight to send me home before these issues could escalate any further.

And he was right, I didn't take an overdose as soon as I got home.

Part Two

I found myself back in the bin. This time, I was kept in nearly a month and was referred to my local Community Mental Health Team when I was discharged.

I quickly got an letter inviting me to attend an appointment with a psychiatrist. I arrived at the appointment, fully expecting to be signed off work for the foreseeable future and to be presented with details of claiming sickness benefit. In my naivety, I had resigned from my stressful job months earlier and had been existing on my savings, oblivious to the fact that I was probably entitled to some assistance.

I was mistaken. He advised me to return to working immediately. I flipped out (again!). How could he expect me to cope with working when I couldn't manage to wash myself in the morning? How could yet another trained professional miss the fact that I was falling apart on the inside? Why when my friends who were as screwed up as I was were signed off work for months at a time, was I expected to manage working and having a breakdown at the same time? Why did they all hate me so much? Again, I raged to anyone that would listen that he obviously hated me and was trying to kill me, and that he'd be sorry when I did kill myself.

Nevertheless, I signed on with a temping agency and was given a data entry job. It was mindless work and didn't challenge me at all; it did, however, provide me with structure, an identity outside that of "mental health service user" and an opportunity to develop friendships and self-esteem. It was a struggle, but eighteen months later, my confidence had increased sufficiently that I felt able to move into a field that was more interesting to me. Four years later, I have a job that I love, that I'm good at and that gives me immense satisfaction.

I can't help but doubt that things would have panned out the same way if I had been dismissed with a 'sick note.'

I wish I had the opportunity to go back to these psychiatrists and say 'thank you, you did know what was right for me, more than I did at the time, I'm sorry for reacting how I did.'

I don't dispute that there are health care professionals who don't always get it right or who convey a sense of indifference or frustration. However, I don't believe that they are the group of incompetent, uncaring fuckwits that service users sometimes cast them as.

Princess Prozac
Brita

Little capsule white and green
Wonder drug or magic bean
A public life filled with wealth
In privacy poor mental health;
Were you pushed?
Or did you fall?
Just pop that pill
It cures all
Psychiatrist's chair
Prescription pad
Princess Prozac
Let's be mad;
Happy land we never cry
Prozac in our water supply
Forget morphine and cocaine
Legal drugs will keep you sane;

Princes Prozac is smiling now
Blood and sweat
Have left her brow;
Little capsule green and white
Help poor princess sleep at night.

When Medication Stops Helping
Anonymous

I stumbled across an old photograph of me mid undress yesterday. My boyfriend and I had spent the weekend together, I was in the middle of getting dressed for a night out with our friends and was oblivious to the fact that he'd captured this moment. I didn't recognise that girl at first. She was full of sparkle and hope. Excited about life and looking forward to what was round the corner. Deliriously in love. Enveloped in a wide circle of friends. She was also nine stone.

Various factors, circumstances and my inherent vulnerabilities culminated to pull me into a new world of despair, despondency and pain. I lost my sparkle, I lost my hope, I lost my will to live. This inevitably resulted in the loss of many important people in my life. A suicide attempt later, I was enveloped in the local mental health services and was introduced to a cocktail of medication. I was also introduced to stretch marks, 'fat' shops and verbal abuse from strangers. In just two years, I had been prescribed six different tablets and had put on just over a stone for each.

While I accept that psychiatric medication plays an important role in minimising a range of distressing symptoms, I strongly believe attention needs to be paid to the side effects of these drugs and their long-term consequences. Weight gain is one of many undesirable side effects of psychiatric medication.

Psychiatric medication may address suicidal ideation, psychosis and agitation in the short-term, but in many cases, it is surely introducing a new set of problems. In the long-term, obesity is associated with numerous health conditions; diabetes, heart disease and joint problems, to name a few. We are also aware of the role that low self-esteem plays in mental health problems. Surely piling on the pounds (or stones!) is only going to exacerbate poor self-esteem and its detrimental effects on mental well-being. Is it any wonder that compliance with medication is often poor?

I'm no longer in denial that my weight gain was entirely due to my medication, I accept that for every pound that was from the drugs, another pound was down to my actions. But, is this a surprise? Who feels motivated to stick to a diet, when they've piled on a stone in a fortnight? Who feels able to exercise when their anti-psychotics have left them so lethargic that it's a struggle to get out of bed of a morning. If you're battling with these issues, as well as your mental health problems, it's understandably tempting to give up and comfort yourself with a packet of chocolate digestives.

It's about time that we all acknowledge and address the issues surrounding weight gain as a side effect of psychiatric medication. Prescribers must recognise that not only can weight gain damage the already fragile self-esteem of the person taking the medication, it can also contribute to long-term problems. They must respond to the concerns of service users with the sensitivity and respect this issue deserves. Manufacturers must develop a wide range of psychiatric medication, in order to give prescribers and service users several options. And finally, service users must be honest and assertive about their needs, lifestyle and how their medication is affecting them.

As for me, I long to be 'that girl' again; I wonder which will be more of a challenge. Regaining the sparkle and hope. Or losing the weight.

Circle of Friends
Mick Burke

An old acquaintance is back in town,
Wearing his familiar long black gown,
He says he's here to teach me a lesson,
And he goes by the name of Severe Depression.

He's brought a friend along this time,
They can come together or wait in line,
This dark double act are crippling me,
Depression and his old mate Anxiety.

Together they make a formidable team,
Coming at me, headlights full beam,
But don't worry or fret, no bloody final act,
For I have my trusty shield, my good friend Seroxat.

Seroxat has some relatives, Prozac I've met,
And most doctors agree, either one's a good bet,
"A proven fact that SSRIs are a wonderful family,
Even take them myself, so's the wife occasionally."

So armed with the drugs upon your side,
Deeper in to the mire you surely can't slide,
But I have to inform, with deepest regret,
That old D and A, they aren't finished yet.

I sincerely hope this grizzly pair never pay you a
                                        visit,
But if they do, think poetry, and show them where
                                        to sit.
Depression, he's very quiet, although Anxiety's
                            staring may annoy you,
Don't worry, get another chair, he's brought his
                            brother, Paranoia.

The Search
Mick Burke

Where should I look?
Outside? Within?
If you stay very still,
You're overcome by the din.

I know! A G.P.
He'll have the answer,
It comes as a tablet,
To avoid a disaster.

C.P.N.? Consultant,
A therapist maybe,

52

They all treat depression,
But which one will treat me?

Giving up? Giving in?
It's not really an option,
Get back to the Doctor,
For another fine potion.

The N.H.S., a mental solution

2. Everyday Life with Borderline Personality Disorder

Beginnings

Cold Lino
Dianne Aslett

Woking
smokey
pokey was where
I was born,
a Surrey town
then Chertsey
dirty, fell in the river
all of a shiver
scared and uncared for
on cold, lino floor
toys all around
crying and scolded,
shocked and locked in
the madness forever,
a rock and a hard place
trying to save face
I struggled and bumped
without warning
one morning
into a lamppost
my brother led me
treading not carefully
enough
I wasn't tough,

I remember the big bump
on my forehead
my mum putting butter on it
Was that a fit thing to do?
I don't know
but I grew
and I worried, always worried
and buried my worries
deeper to add more,
what was life for?
I never knew.

I had nightmares
she'd glare at me
coming into my bedroom
'go to sleep
I don't want a peep
out of you' or
if in a good mood,
'come into our bed'
as I cried I was led
there, cosy and warm
until the next storm.

Cranleigh at seven
was like heaven
when we got there
so clean and posh
though I was scared
about the new
and hid to escape the move
but of course
we went
and I made friends,
primrosing the farms
in those days

far from harm it seemed
sweet summers
riding my bike
highjumping
and scrumping,

And when came the snow
we'd throw snowballs
falling off sledges
icicles in our ears,
my uncle and aunt
and spoilt cousin Jonathon
who I hated, but still
we DID things with them
went places when
my family did little,
·just stayed home
feeling alone
and longing for
some inspiration
when there was so much
castigation
and fear
in my house
there were always tears
and insecurity
manipulations and dread.

I wondered about death
What happened to the dead?
always wondered
and the world was odd,
I thought about God
a lot.

Tripping Home

Dianne Aslett

On the bus
silken-faced grammar boys
tread firmly, eyes
ahead
uncurious of us,
knowing their worth.

These boys:
fine-clad and clean,
smart,
robust, a breed apart,
manner's ease
the pleasure of
the cream of genes
and an innocence of wily ways. Of
these, no need. Like gods,
their radiance foreshadows
futures blessed.

I watch them,
not envious only, but
inspired,
wish my sense of self
like theirs,
the natural graciousness,
the solidity of stature,
working with the world's rules and all,
ancestral formulae
delete the question,
forestall the conflict.

I listen to them.

Speech concise, well-defined,
strikes the air.
No hesitation here.
Grooving to success,
well-fingered, clear -
you do this, do that
and step by step
well, you're there.

I imagine parents
who care, are aware,
can warn of world's danger, greed,
unholy creeds.
I think of
kind concern and
confidence won, of
intelligence and
common sense in all that's done.

Intimacy,
Protection, yes,
And even Love.

These boys,
I watch them,
warm to them.

Something in me rises
to their kind,
relates, cries, identifies
yet cannot grasp or integrate.

Here I am, decades on
still the outsider,
this world so wholesome
longing to assume.

The Aspirant, always,
roaming,
languishing for lack
of the nourishment
on which they feed.

I watch them
kindly alien yet
full of angst.

The bus jolts.

I move in magic
clandestinely under
their skin,
Transfigured, tripping home.

Who Will Come?
Celia

The child cries out
Sobs reaching into the blackness,
But no one listens, nobody comes.
The child is alone.

A sound on the stairs
A creak of the floorboards
The crying stops, the child looks up;

He smiles

He comes
No word is needed

The child motionless
Petrified
Buries her face.

You - Why?
Judy Aldridge

You wrecked my body and you wrecked my brain,
You really tried to drive me insane.

You did to me what was not your right,
You are a bastard of the night.

You took my respect along with my pride,
You have not paid for the tears I have cried.

You made me hate and that I will always regret,
You have not even asked for my forgiveness yet.

You made me bitter and so very scared,
You who my body and soul lay bared.

You killed in me all the love that I had,
You're not sorry and you're not even mad.

You made me hurt and badly bleed,
You violated me with your obnoxious seed.

You thought I was dead and you were nearly right,
You did not know how for my life I would fight.

You who God will punish in his own way,
You will have to face your judgement day.

You are so cunning and so very sly,
You make me sit and wonder, WHY?

Untitled
Celia

She had been here before, a long time ago, yet it was like yesterday. It had been different then, the house had been busy, important, full of the hustle and bustle of everyday living, and him.

She could hear her name being called from the house but she remained sitting on the swing at the far end of the garden. No one could touch her there, or so it felt, she was invincible, in a bubble, totally alone. The voice called her name again but still she ignored it, feeling the panic rising within her. If she pretended not to hear perhaps they would leave her alone, forget about her.

She wanted to run and hide but experience had taught her that there was no hiding place that was secret now, they had discovered them all, except the one in her mind.

'Please don't let them find me.'

She half turned towards the house and saw a figure standing at the window right at the top. It stood, motionless and watched her. Her blood ran cold in her veins; she knew that there would be no escape. Bile rose in her throat.

Turning away, she pushed herself as hard as she could, making the swing go higher and higher. 'I'm not really here' she chanted to herself, trying to calm her frantic thoughts. She prayed that it was all part of a dream, that she would wake up, safe, and all this would be gone, forever. Higher and higher, but her thoughts came with her.

Daring to look back at the house again, she saw the figure had gone from the window but was now outside, at the corner of the house, walking slowly towards her. Higher still she pushed herself. Her mind was screaming at her now, begging her to flee, but there was no escape.

For a moment she became lost in the motion of the swing. If only she could stay high enough, stay forever out of reach.

One last look. The figure almost upon her. One more push, she had to try just once more. So high now, surely even they could not touch her here. She could almost reach out and touch the clouds, fly with the birds. No one would hurt her ever again. A blinding light, her name being called over and over. Then there was nothing, not even blackness.

It was different now. The house just a shell. She had left it long ago. Now there was peace, only the stirring of leaves where there was no wind.

Fragments
Elle Jay

Shadows of the past float by like sullied dreams
Not knowing what is true or what just seems
Too real, too false, too painful to recall
Too wrong to lie, too hard to forget all

Mists of time descend and cloak your face
Your touch that froze me solid stays in place
But was it you or does my mind deceive?
Some twisted plot for mercy to conceive?

Trapped inside the mystery of my past
I find a way to soothe the pain, at last
My blood flows free in pulsing bright red streams
Silencing my inner haunted screams

I'll never know the day that autumn came
The day things ceased to be just quite the same
This winter's tale now left to time to mend
I know that it began, but will it end?

I thought it seemed as if you didn't care
Should I forgive? Or were you even there?
And if you weren't, another story grows
But which is true? I wish I knew who knows...

Halfway up the Stairs
Brita

Looking down at my small white ankle socks
I'm meant to be in bed, but again I'm sitting on a
                                                    stair
Trying so hard not to listen, but I need to be sat
                                                    here
Every night I'm sitting there, every night I'm sitting
                                                    there.

The voices rise sharply, the noise grows and grows
I can pick out some things and sometimes hear my
                                                    name

The door isn't open, so the words are never clear
But one thing I'm sure of, I'm somehow to blame.

The silences are the hardest, and make me shake
                                                with fear
I find them unsettling and I begin to cry
I'm certain that they have started fighting
And this time one will die.

"Why did you have to drink today?"
"Why didn't you wash my shirt?"
"When are you going to pay off credit bills?"
And "You know we live in dirt!"

The "name calling" is what follows:
"Bitch", "slut", "dog" and "whore"
Then I KNOW one of them will try to leave
And make a run to the door
Then the usual is there may be some stumbling
Which can stop with a loud thud.
But I daren't go down to see though
I'm scared to see mummy's blood.

The daily fights upset me, and mummy shouldn't
                                                drink
I want to run away myself, run far away
But if I leave our house, NOT "Home"
Mummy'll be dead that day,
She just won't cope alone.

Untitled
Celia

You steal in quietly, softly, as goose-down to
                         embrace
Lest anyone should notice the fingers of steel
The vice grip of damnation lying cold in the grave
Holding your victim forever in this space.

Never are you welcome in this hallowed place
But still insinuate venom thrust deep within
To devour and embezzle all spirit, all hope
Energy to distort, maim, break, never to heal.

You with the power to tear all apart
An unleashed beast within life's very core
You devour as if to never eat again
Leaving tatters and shreds strewn upon the floor.

Defenceless I face you, yet cannot see
Your malevolent evil, so bitterly disguised
In panic and emptiness, in bitter regret
Covetous anger lies deep in the breast.

You have taken life and buried it
Mangling, wrenching, ripping, tearing apart
Stone cold, with no feeling,
Until faceless it doth appear.

All manner is down now, no way to repair
Disparate parts flung into the last box
Now to lie forever, buried and raped
Humanity spent, six feet in the ground.

The Child
Karen

She sits there
Staring out of the window
Longing to escape
Dreaming of another world.

Her body quivers
Trembles
Flinches at the pain
Crumpled up
Like an old newspaper
Trying to ignore the aching.

Eyes wide open
Swimming with tears
Fighting to stop them brimming over
Scared of the raging anger
The hatred
Frightened of herself.

She longs for comfort
For warmth
For someone to heal the wounds
To scoop her up
Make it all better
Protect her from the world.

Her head full of possibilities
Imagining what freedom looks like
Craving a place of refuge
Solace.

But the voice pulls her back
Jerks her into reality
Into the cold, dark, lonely world

In which she must battle for survival
An alien in a foreign land
A misfit
A world in which
She is no longer innocent
No longer trusting
Not safe.

Too many lies told
Too much damage done
The flickering light of hope
Gradually fading.

In Search of Self

All I Want
Mick Burke

The only thing I want is,
Something I cannot see,
It cannot be bought, borrowed or loaned,
The only thing I want is.... me.

I had it once, or so I thought,
Not all that long ago,
But it drifted away to a place deep inside,
All that's left seems like insanity.

I want it back, of that I'm sure,
Although it seems an impossible dream,
And end to the punishment, isolation,
A pass to whatever is 'normality'.

The Stranger, Who Is Me?
Celia

Who are you, who gazes out
From deep within the mirror?
I know there should be recognition
But only see the stranger.

Long black lashes framing
Big hazel-brown eyes,
They hide so well the pain and hurt
That exists behind the mask.

Hidden thoughts, a hidden world
Others can never see.
What is real to you, and you?
Is not my reality.

Who am I?
Beverley 09/04

I am:
The slasher, the cutter, the burner, the head banger, the biter, the swallower, the screamer, the shouter, the druggy, the piss artist, the destroyer; the OD in cubicle three.

I am:
Here, yet again. The time waster, the naughty and hopeless case, the pain in the arse, the crisis queen, the attention seeker, the unfit, the sad, the lonely, the nutter; the head case down the road.

I am:
The weak minded, the stupid, the sicko, the deceitful, the manipulative, the failure, the lonely, the desperate, the inferior, the flawed; the scared and the scarred.

I am:
Judged and guilty as charged. To be gossiped about, frowned upon, nervously smiled at, ignored, rebuffed, laughed at, pitied, avoided, told off: spoken to sternly.

I am:
Who I am.

I am:
Misunderstood.

I am:
The parent, the partner, the relation, the friend, the giver, the listener, the protector, the carer, the lover, the wit, the teacher, the supporter, the motivator, the homemaker, the volunteer, the worrier, the planner, the organiser; oh yes –

I am:
The patient.

I am:
The tryer, the talker, the singer, the mover, the dancer, the painter, the gardener, the writer, the explorer; the survivor.

Like the Water Lily, whose roots are sunk deep in the wet, cold, dark mud and silt, one day too, I want all this filth to feed *beautiful* blooms.

Am I:
Understood?

I Am That I Am
Dianne Aslett

There are people who have loved me
There are people who have cared
And Truth was There -
The space so secret
Silent, touched
Where Pain and Joy intertwine
And grip in strain

70

So sensitive
And kind
The Reality
That Is Me.

There are persons whereby we've met
And understood It All It All
And understood It All - and yet

The Vision shifted, shifts
And I am left
Alone again
And never really known.

And when - Oh is there a 'when'?
When All Will Be Revealed?
I do believe
Out of necessity perhaps -
Out of the grief

That eschaton Is.
And I 'Know'
Because
'I Am'

And this
No counselling skill
Can show

Amen
Let It Be So
Let It Be So....

The Mirror
Dawn Whalley

When I look in the mirror – what is it I see?
A wreck with no soul looking back at me.
Ugly, self-inflicted scars cover my body
A head hung in shame for all to see
When I look in the mirror – that's me, that's me.

When I look in the mirror – what do I think?
I'm ugly, I'm bad – constantly on the brink
Of feeling my life has no meaning.
I'm so misunderstood.
Negativity, black + white thinking all flood
My brain and overwhelm me.
Constantly setting myself up to fail.
A perfectionist who can never achieve.
A life so perfect that can never be.
When I look in the mirror – that's what I think.

When I look in the mirror – what do I feel?
Life has no meaning – it's just not real.
I'm too sensitive, I feel all of life's pain
I have no energy – I am drained.
I care too much – I can't help it.
I feel everyone's pain which digs my own pit
                              deeper and deeper.
Just one step further and I'll jump.
I'm overwhelmed with emotions with which I can't
                                        cope
Emotions so powerful – is there any hope?

I am what I am – will I ever change?
Conditioned through childhood memories and pain.
Psychology, psychiatry and pills galore
Is that what I want? Do I want more?
At the end of the day I need to 'find me'.

72

To accept myself, my personality
And give myself time to heal.
When I look in the mirror – that's what I feel.

Pieces
Ashman

There are pieces of me all over the world:

There are sketches in London,
There are scribbles in Kent,
There's a painting in Essex
And some songs that I sent;
There's a tape in Newcastle
And a jacket as well
And my echo's been heard
In the Station Hotel;
There's an old friend in Catford,
And several in Leeds,
And poetry scattered
Like sunflower seeds;
There are memories in Thailand
And more in Nepal,
And under the paint
There's my name on a wall;
Yeah, there are pieces of me
All over the place,
But here in my mind,
Of me, there's no trace.

The Reality Within

Alone
Celia

You only see
The painted façade
That I let you see.
Behind the cracked mask
Great chasms lie,
The walls fall round my feet.

Even when I let you
Peer through the chinks
You will never see,
The deep, disastrous pain
That pierces my soul,
Into eternity.

You try to see hope
Where none exists
If reality be faced.
I know I cannot live my days
With this burden
That will not be shared.

If You Could See Me Now
Anonymous

if you could see me now
stumbling
choking

bleeding
crying
gagging

dying

if you could see me now
you wouldn't have me back

but
if you could see me now
you might just believe
that it really is *this* bad

Think Of Other Things
Gail Silver

Whenever I am at my work,
I never seem to care;
To worry about problems
Which are always there.

I laugh and joke so happily
And give a cheerful smile.
But underneath my smiling face
I worry all the while.

But for the moment, there is no worry;
No worrying nor pain
But as soon as I am on my own
The sadness comes again.

I think of things that might have been;
Of things that are to come.

Of people I might one day meet
But now I stand alone.

I stand alone in all I do.
At least I feel I do.
For no one's there to comfort me
To truly love me too.

I thought that I was loved just once.
But now I bear the pain
As I bore it yesterday:
I'm all alone again

But surely one day I will find
Someone to take my hand.
To take me from my world of dreams
And make my real life grand.

But now I've pondered long enough
On things that might have been.
I must think of other things in life
And stop my childish dreams!

A Gaping Whole
Elle Jay

And they laugh and they smile and they look at me
and I wonder if they can see me. Is there a me for
them to see?

And they laugh and they smile and they look at me
and I wonder if any one of them stretched out an
arm would it go straight through me? What is there
here to stop it?

76

The whole world laughs and smiles whilst I live like a shadow, a cloud, an ambiguous entity with no end and no beginning, a function of circumstance, the shape of my container, an amorphous collection of matter that indistinctly belongs to this thing called 'me'. Self is an illusion, an illusion I don't suffer. There is no me, just a hole where a 'me' should be. A painful hole. A thick and solid empty space.

If I take this hole and make it me, what then will I be but defined by nothing?

Protection
Karen

Must keep everything in
Must remain in control
Don't let it out
Don't open the door
Release the floodgates.

Build the wall
Keep filling in the gaps
Cement is falling out
Bricks missing.

Wall starting to crumble
Must repair it
Must maintain it
Hold it strong
Not let anything out
Not let anyone in.

But I can't do it anymore

Fighting a losing battle
Wall is breaking down
People will see what's inside
Mustn't let them discover it
Must keep up the barrier.

Don't let people near
Don't let them get close
Might find out too much
Might get hurt
Mustn't find out
Must maintain the mask
Keep up the pretence.

But what is it that's inside?
What is it that I am so desperate to defend?

Circles

Josie

Going around in circles,
Never knowing when it will stop,
Never knowing when it will end
And I can be me again.

And the circles get smaller
Instead of bigger
And I feel more trapped,
More enclosed,
More confused and controlled.

I often wonder if I'll escape –
If I'll jump out and save myself,
Or if I'll stay trapped
Until the circles choke me.

Because there doesn't seem to be an in-between.

Maybe someone will pull me out
And rescue me from this mess.
But I'd have to scream for help, first,
And I'm not sure I can.

That would be admitting that
I can't cope
And I can't do that.

The mask must never fall,
The voice must never falter,
The cracks must never show.

I must keep on pretending
That I like circles

But I don't.

Self-Destruction

Impulsive Tendencies
Ashman

Buy it
sell it
eat it
drink it
take it
give it
lose it
fake it
break it
make it
smash it
crash it
drop it
chuck it
fix it
fuck it!

Battlefield
E. Thurston

On this battlefield called Life
I stand cut and bruised, a casualty
Of my own internal war
Scars litter my body and mind
Memories of past conflicts fought
I reflect upon deeper wounds
Injuries that never quite heal

But I must continue fighting
For there is no magic answer
To take my pain away.

Untitled
Ruth

Self-harm does more than scar my arms. It leaves a permanent mark on my mind. It carries the message each time that I am worth no more than this and deserve to be hurt. My self-esteem sinks at the same time as the blade.

The self-injury came to the surface only when I was being treated for my eating disorder. I felt that 'they' – the staff – had taken all control away from me by making me eat. I cut as a reaction to this – I was retaliating. 'They' could force me to put on weight but I had something else up my sleeve.

While being treated in a local hospital for my weight loss I dug my heels in when it came to reaching six stone. I would not go any higher. I did opt to go to an eating disorders unit. It bought me more time out of life and reality. There my cutting worsened since I was eating more food than before where calories had been increased with supplement drinks. The hospital threatened to discharge me at the same time as I wanted to stay there for longer.

Ten years after starting to harm myself I still do it though it is under control. I have had admissions because of serious self-harm. The only effect of being in hospital away from blades was that it gave my body time to recover. I felt frustrated and that staff did not notice me because I do not have a psychotic illness.

Self-injury still serves a purpose. It is a form of self-expression that I have created or at least adapted in a personal way. I am marking myself, making me different from others. Making those who I know concerned about me. It is a way of showing that I am unwell. I feel I need to cut to be a genuine case for services because of the way other people view my diagnosis. The cutting involves emotion when I feel numb. At the same time it is hellish. I dread cutting because I know there will be pain and I probably will not be able to do it the way I want to. It is self-harm on top of self-harm – it never ends.

When I am in a cycle of cutting I feel energised – as though I am running on adrenaline. As though I can get 'something' right. I go crashing afterwards and the emptiness is heightened.

You will find that self-harm and suicidal gestures are grouped together as one criteria for BPD. They are separate. I cut to feel alright – or at least come to an acceptance – about carrying on with living. I have taken potentially lethal overdoses but have always known whether they were self-injury or a suicide attempt. Usually I have just wanted to express how terrible things were and to hope that after the overdose and antidote treatment I would want to live.

No medication has helped with self-harm except an antipsychotic as a sedative at nights when I most want to cut. Sometimes I get so agitated that I want to be heavily medicated but know it will only make me worry about weight gain and not being in control. Self-harm has to be something I work through and make decisions about.

Mystery Explained

Elle Jay

Bleed because I'm angry
Bleed because I'm sad
Bleed because I'm crazy
Bleed because I'm bad

Bleed because you hate me
Bleed because you don't
Bleed because you love me
Bleed because I won't

Bleed because you left me
Bleed because you stayed
Bleed because you stained me
Bleed because you strayed

Bleed because I'm sorry
Bleed because I'll mend
Bleed because eventually
We're parted in the end...

Certain Little Spells Wake Big Demons
Ashman

Floored again by a certain little spell
I'm lying in Beethoven's 9th Symphonic hell,
Wailing and marking
The hours on my arms
And proving that waiting
Passes the time.

A Few Days Later
Ashman

The blackest day, a cutting mood:
I feel the need to get away
From all of this, and yet,
No matter where I turn my step
A veil remains before my eyes,
Sorrow stains my every thought,
And Yesterday my hope denies.

Foreign…
Elle Jay

I look at these scars,
These useless, pointless scars
And what do I see?
These raised red ridges
Scattered everywhere
Like ladders leading into my heart
A futile and desperate attempt to reach it,
To make a path for someone else to follow
The wounds of battle

When seen altogether
They constitute the whole war
A war which rages on inside of me
They tell my story
But in no coherent way
They show to the whole world
The inner torment
But no one else can read them
No one else speaks my language
Written on me **forever**
Is a tale no one else will ever be able to recount
A sign of survival, perhaps
But mostly just a sign
Of how hard it is to get through each day
Seen or felt, they say the same thing
Each scar tells its own tale
Each shouts out its own pain
Its own hate, its own desperation
They scream so loud
Yet they fall on deaf ears
Unheard, misunderstood
Pointless indeed...

Urge...
Elle Jay

Wash over me, steal me, make me whole. Break
my chains and release me. I don't know why I want
you, I don't know why I feel I need you. The pain,
the sweet, sweet pain, it soothes, it calms, it
comforts. Destroy me, harm me, hurt me, hate me.
Envelop me in the here and now. Awaken the
slumbering beast within and remind me I'm alive.

Show me the meaning everything else lacks. Assure me there is an escape from the torment.

I don't understand your vice-like grip of comfort. Within moments of tasting your sweet sensation an unfamiliar calm predominates. The past and the future fade into the now and there is nothing but the present. The volume dims, the panic subsides. The gentle thud resumes its sedentary pace. My paradise regained on the fringes of hell. A torturous juxtaposition of pleasure and pain. But it's not happiness. No. What is it? It's calm, serenity, freedom and peace. And it's now – just now, nowhen else.

Wash over me, steal me, make me whole. Seal the cracks and smooth the edges. Carry me through and keep me alive.

Help me, just help me make it through…

Bleed Me Free...
An ode to Self-Injury
Elle Jay

Bleed me free, scar me up
Drink from danger's tempting cup
Give me pain, quell the rush
Bring the soothing post-act hush
Stem the hate, cure the fears
See the flowing blood-red tears
Dare the fool, "shhhh" the noise
Let me play with pointy toys
Kick me down, kill my soul
Self destruction is my goal

Drain me off, make me sad
Purge the good and leave the bad
Boil me dry, starve me thin
Free the pent up rage within
Close your eyes, turn around
Let me run myself aground
Hurt me **please**, scratch me raw
Shred my mind and make it sore
Set me loose, let me go
Forget the world and all I know

But for fuck's sake
Love me not, just leave me be
Then stand and let me bleed me free.

Cut Burn Out
Brita

When the tears stop flowing
Does the pain stop hurting?
When the skin starts healing
Is the mind better now?
Can it really forgive?

They all stop listening
When the smile disappears
They all turn away
When the eyedrops start glistening
Just don't let them see your scars.

No one sees the hidden tears of pain
The claret flow of expensive wine
Slowly a bright red river grows
Spreading quickly on the skin

Dripping everywhere; flowing too fast
Eyes dried up, as blood more private
Hidden from others, under clothing
The burn of a cut keeps me alive
This time pricked by a fucking rose
Pain once more – can't cut it out.

Untitled
Ruth

I am hungry for love. I feel deprived of touch.

The cause of my many difficulties is an emotional
void. It spreads and kills the life I should have.

Starving it out of myself through anorexia was a
temporary solution. It worked while I could maintain
it. By eating less I was making food special. And
myself special. I created a whole new inner world of
food, weight and exercise – words repeating
themselves over and over again in my head. When
eating just breadcrumbs each day my plight was
self-evident. I could not be ignored – I was dying.
Other people paid attention. When an inpatient
being re-fed it felt like my emotional needs were
getting met. I did not have to make any decisions
and my food was given to me. Permission to eat. It
was like being a child again and nurtured. At the
same time I dreaded the weight gain since this
reversed what I had achieved. The trait that got me
noticed was being erased and corrected. I saw
others as fattening me up taking the only way I
knew how to cope with the emptiness.

All that was until the bingeing started. Now I shove food down barely tasting it. I try to satisfy the hunger inside me – but it does not work. I do not dare go without food for long because I will feel hungry, which will remind me of the emptiness within. I am confused about when I have eaten enough and when I need to eat. I swallow cheap biscuits I do not even like. As soon as I have swallowed something I have to grab other food. I cannot have a moment's rest from the eating. Being physically bloated reminds me of how out of control I am. It is a time when I do not want others to see me.

Reality
Anonymous

What is disordered eating?

It's lying to your friends and family.
It's saying 'no' to nights-out in case they expect you to eat.

It's praying your heart doesn't stop if you miscalculate the amphetamines.
It's shitting yourself 'cos you've overdone the laxatives.

It's stealing food out of the bin.
It's exceeding your overdraft to buy food you won't taste.

It's constant pains in your teeth.
And constant pains in your gut.

It's being suicidal if you've gained half a pound, and
being suicidal if you've *only* lost half a pound.

And they say it's all about having control.
I don't think I've ever had less control.

Candy
Suzanne Lowe

The game is over,
It is time.
The door locked, my prize safely hidden.
The goldfish gape as I open the drawer.

I never knew I had so much choice!
An array of boxes, colours, names –
I can't help but smile.
It all goes tonight.

I take my time and begin with the red –
My favourite! I savour the bitterness right
Down to my stomach.
It makes me hungry, greedy for more.

Suddenly the control is gone,
I cram handfuls into my mouth,
A bulimic binge - I know I will vomit soon,
But everything must go!
It must be tonight.

But in one moment, one mistake
Signals the destruction of my plan.
The telephone, once my saviour,
Shrieks and cackles,

The funereal sound of discovery.

This is my downfall.
As tears and vomit mingle,
My stomach contracting painfully,
The green man appears and whisks me away,
The end of the adventure,
Signposted by the smell of bleach, disinfectant
And sickness.

Lying on the trolley, a man in blue draws near.
"Well well" he says, as the needle pierces the skin.
"Didn't you know too much candy is bad for you?"

Relationships

Darling, I've Been Bleeding
Ashman

Whilst you sleep,
Pale and dreaming
Caressed by pressed black sheets
And draped in misty lace:

Darling, I've been bleeding.

As you dream
Of lovers lost and found,
Of festivals and masked charades
And quests of endless seeking:

Darling, I've been bleeding.

Whilst you lie
Hungry and panting,
Frantically grinding,
Ecstatically hiding:

Darling, I've been bleeding.

Marks of Weakness, Marks of Woe
Ashman

Look beneath my arm my love,
And if you're sharp you'll see
A thousand lines that mark the time
Since you abandoned me.

The cruellest words I ever heard
In sickness or in health:
"I can't make love to someone
Who could do that to himself."

The Wreck of the Gemini
for KA
Ashman

Shipwrecked and stranded
Flung half-mad and broken,
Forgotten and forsaken
By those we thought loved;
Lonely and crying
And so weary of trying,
Of losing, of searching,
Of never quite finding.
Scared of beginnings
And crushed by the endings,
Teased by a dream
That has flown with the day.
Taunted by phantoms
'Til screaming and praying
We flee down the paths
That we know fade away.

So. Shipwrecked and lonely
The hole that can only
Be filled by the arms
That will never forsake
Screams out for fulfillment
But half mad and broken
We seek without knowing
How long it will take.

If Only You Knew
Ashman

If I voiced the thoughts within my head
I'm sure that you'd leap out of bed
And grab your clothes from off the floor,
Then flee downstairs and out the door.

The Friend
Gail Silver

You who helped me when I was unhappy.
You who looked beyond the cover to my mind
-- My secret mind.
You who saw what lay behind that gay façade.
You who tried to unlock the door.
But, it was barred – chained and bolted.
Unable to be opened – not even by me.
How can anyone find the key which I have lost?
I have tried, and failed.

Several came after me; their endeavours insincere.
But you, in all your ignorance of the mind
Tried and tried. Time was not with you.
And as it sped unceasingly by – so did I.
Now, is the key lost forever?
Once it was nearly yours, to unlock the door.
But time, the enemy, ruled supreme,
And the key slipped further into the abyss of my
                                        mind.
Gone! Sinking deeper! What could I do?
And now, another enemy!
The realization that I had not been truly honest with
                                        myself.
I was hiding inside my imagination.

Now grounded – almost back to full reality.
What was it that worried my turmoiled brain?
You nearly had the answer.

But now, in the coldness of a new day,
Loneliness ensues.
Hours upon hours roll across my memory of times
                                        gone by.
Times when perhaps I was happy. Or is that a lie
                                        too?
Now, I know its fateful road – the ugly head of
                                        loneliness.
The uncertainty and insecurity.

You have weathered stormy seas
And come out at the other end
Now sailing in much calmer weather.
I? I am still at battle.
What shall I do?
Must I drown alone
Never to find the key –
The key to my mind?

Thank you for your endeavours.
A true friend?
I am not worthy.
Forgive me.
I go!

Love
Ashman

I speak of love,
I sing of love,
I feel it in my dreams;
I swear that you inspire it
But I don't know what it means.

Elusive
Elle Jay

Your twisted motives tied me tight
You caught me in your snare
And so I ran to find the light
Of someone else's lair...

Backfired
Elle Jay

I risked my heart, I laid it out,
Exposed I left it there
For you to take and to caress,
Administer some care
I know its state was somewhat rough;
Its chambers small & sickly,
But did you have to give it back
Just quite so bloody quickly?!

I Once Knew A Girl
Ashman

I once knew a girl from Huddersfield
(Or somewhere thereabouts)
Who fed her cat on sirloin steak
And filled my head with doubts.

I once knew a girl from Osbaldwick
Who never knew what to do:
So I sent her a letter to make me feel better
And set off to find someone new.

I once knew a nurse from Sheffield
Who I'm sure had a secret to tell:
But I left her one day on a May motorway
And secured my damnation in Hell.

I once knew a girl from Colwyn Bay
With a ring in her nose like a pig:
She was mad as they come and she lent me a gun
But she filled all the holes I could dig.

I once knew a girl from Middlesbrough
Who burbled and gushed like a stream:
But she realised one day, and then soon ran away
With a cuckoo she met in a dream.

I once knew a girl from Trumpington,
Which is somewhere near Camberwick Green:
She was shy as a mole and filled up her hole
With more books than I've ever seen.

I once knew a girl from Lancashire,
A place that is bad for your health,
And the War of the Roses began with disclosures
That I was from Yorkshire meself.

I once knew a girl from Æorwic
(That's Saxon for 'York' don't you know)
And if we'd never met, I'm willing to bet,
That these scars on my arms wouldn't show.

I once knew a girl from Newcastle
And I'm sure that she was the first
To love me and see all the things that I see,
So why did I treat her the worst?

These girls from the past that are scattered
Have one thing in common you see,
Though all of them passed through the bedroom
Not one of them ever knew me.

CD Problems
Ashman

These things drive me to the brink...

The tap-tap-tap of the keys
That struggle to drown-out the thoughts
That torment and tempt and tease.
Tap-tap-tap
Tapping your name
Tap-tap-tap
Again and again
And again and again.
Rewind all the things I did
And play them back and analyse

And play them back and Anna lies
And play them back and anal-eyes,
Now press <DELETE>
Error: Read only file
Hit space to continue...
<SPACE>
Cut and copy and paste
Access denied
Then try erase
Hard disk full
You what??
<DELETE> I say
I can't it says
Love.sys is write protected
Love.sys is a hidden file
Operating System
Needs reinstalling...

<CTRL><ALT><DELETE>

Untitled

Anonymous

Where is it that you've gone to?
Why didn't you say you were leaving?
Perhaps you did,
Perhaps those were the words you so silently
murmured;
The ones I was too tired to hear.
Now I scream; silently, deafeningly
But you're not there to hear me.
You can't hear me say I want to know, I want to
listen.
You can't hear me say I'm sorry.

I'm awake now, I'm here now.
But here is truly gone. I've missed you.
You don't even know I came to say goodbye.
But if somehow you can hear me tonight,
I'm sorry I was too late,
I miss you now it's you who's late,
I love you.
I wonder if one day we'll be in the same place at the
                                                    same time,
I wonder if we'll see each other, hear each other.
I wonder what you'll see
I wonder if you'll love me too.

Coventry
Ashman

Each time I hear them speak of you
Of how you're looking fine and well,
Of how they saw you last weekend
But nothing more will tell,
My jealous heart keeps asking why
Your name alone is offered me?
Did I behave so very wrong
To earn this trip to Coventry?

X to the Power 25
Ashman

My ex wants me in hospital,
My ex ex wants me dead,
My ex ex ex wants my child,
Or so I thought she said.

My third - no, fourth - ex seems to want
Some in depth explanation,
Or better yet to see me hang
For callous exploitation.
My favourite ex just wants to see
Me get back on the track --
But none of them, I don't expect,
Will ever want me back.

Despair

What Kind of Living is This?
Donna Eaton

This mind never rests,
Filled with unwelcome guests,
No intentions of leaving,
While torment conceiving,
What kind of living is this?

This mind keeps debating,
Its value berating,
Self-worth's easy prey,
Trapped in ruthless foul play,
What kind of living is this?

This mind lives in fear,
Of the voices it hears,
Chatter crescendos; screams in the head,
No wonder this soul's crying out to be dead,
What kind of living is this?

This mind is on fire,
Burnt by thoughts that transpires,
From ashes to dust,
Any embers of trust,
What kind of living is this?

This mind grasps brief highs,
Then plunges and cries,
Stuck in black and white thinking,
Rationality's shrinking,
What kind of living is this?

This mind's had enough,
Of life being this tough,
So desperately tired,
All hope has expired,
What kind of living is this?

Happy Days
Brita

Grey clouds filled with rain,
Scar tissue and blades of pain;
Cheap alcohol in a cheap place,
A veil of make-up on my face;
Empty eyes that show no fear,
Mortal sinners gather here;
Empty cans and bottles of wine,
Stay awake and wait in line;
Not a poison but a bitter flavour,
Sweeter thoughts I find my saviour.

The others here lie to impress,
My respect goes from less to less;
Grey clouds fly away in time,
Soul-mate or partner in crime;
The highs are always followed by lows,
Gramme becomes grain, and bitter sweet goes,
Back on land grey clouds return,
Bleeding hearts will never learn;
Scar tissue and lines of pain,
Darkened eyes
Full of rain....

A Dark Night with BPD (1)

Josie

Early hours of Wednesday morning – no idea what time. I wake up, sprawled on my bed. Stuff everywhere – tangle of duvet, pillows, cushions and clothes. At some point I must have got it together because there's a cup of tea on the floor by the bed, gone cold. My throat is stinging. I feel swollen and sick. I realise I must have been crying for a while, because my face feels streaked and tight. I don't want this for myself. No one wants this for themselves.

A Dark Night with BPD (2)

It's night again, and I'm scared. I don't know what I'm doing. Only that I'm not in control, and I don't like that. I don't know how I'm going to get through and reach the morning, and even if I do, what do I do then? Tomorrow will be just the same, only I'll be that bit more tired, more lonely, more depressed, more desperate.

I've been thinking about death again, and it seems so inviting. It would be such a relief. I see it as wrapping myself in something soft and warm and comfortable and black, and sinking into a deep relaxing sleep, never having to wake up and deal with my life or the world again. It would be like a cocoon around me, and I would effortlessly slip down through the layers to reach the bottom, so I couldn't fall any further.

I can hear a voice moaning and I'm afraid it's mine. I haven't been able to stop crying for hours, and I'm trying to rock myself to sleep, but this long slow wailing won't stop, and I think it's coming from my soul. I've tried to vomit it up, and tried to cut it out of my skin, but it won't go, and I don't think it will ever stop. I've even tried to drown it in drink, but it's still there. I've been sliding and sliding, and it feels too late to climb back up. Surely this must be the bottom. I can't cope with any more.

It's like some sick parody of Alice in Wonderland, falling down the hole, only I'm not Alice, and there's nothing wonderful about this.

Untitled
Celia

What is this life
Where no reality holds?
Day into night
Blackness to dark.

No cognitive strands,
Confusion reigns.
Catch the thoughts
Drive them away.

Where's the beginning
Without the end?
Locked in my prison
Rooms with no doors.

Thoughts with no meaning
Make words with no sound.
Action without meaning
Swirls constantly round.

Pictures of the Dark
Celia

Darkness falls
But in my mind
There never had been light.
Dread the sleep
For dreams it brings
Within my restless night.

Visions, vivid real
Don't leave my mind
When waking, morning brings,
Enclose my thoughts
Cloak my mind
Confuse reality.

Pursue me through my daylight hours
Fearful of the time
No more avoid the moment when
The night takes on a life.

When once again to face that time
When darkness is no friend.

Way Out
Ashman

Way out it declares,
I wish there was,
Way out in confident type;
But I know that your letters
Are lying to me,
For the exit is nowhere in sight.

106

Falling Like Flies

Ashman

Death and Despair are stalking this town
Sauntering and swaggering through the pubs, clubs
and bars
With their arsenal of whiskey, paracetamol and
razors,
Pushing friends in to rivers and in front of cars.

You maybe can't see them, but some of us can,
Their sharp clipping footsteps ring clear in our ears,
Waiting in ambush in dark lonely moments
They hide in our doubts and pounce out from our
fears.

This reservoir duo that deal in destruction
Are coldly, methodically, hunting us down,
'Til cornered and desperate with nowhere to run to
We're falling like flies in this invalid's town.

Snapshots of My Life

Emma N

27/09
I think I've made a friend :) Went to my course this
evening and a woman called Laura gave me her
phone number and invited me around. Wahey! Ok,
so it's not exactly a huge achievement, but it feels
like it to me. I felt really low, and tired, and not
enthusiastic whatsoever. However afterwards I left
on a high and all because of a little phone number!

18/10

At the moment I'm thinking of Ben and the 6 years since he died. Has my struggling over that time been worth it? I still have a messed up head, I'm still in the Mental Health services, I have nothing to show, my depression's still a constant battle, so is my self-harm and my anger. I don't feel secure anywhere, I dread being alone, I still hate myself and I yearn to belong. I want to be "normal" though I don't know what that is, but also I don't want to become a sheep. In that sense I want to be different, unique, but perhaps without so much baggage. I'd like to feel comfortable with myself, but that feels an impossibility. I remember looking out the window in the stairwell with Ben not long after being there and both of us talking about life and wanting to enjoy it, of what we need to feel well, of feeling trapped in a psychiatric ward.

Ben - was your decision the right one to make?

16/11

I feel in an unreal state. It's like I'm a stranger inside me, looking out into my own world with wonder. It's kind of freaky. Freaking me out and I know that cutting would bring me right back to the present moment. It did last night. Yet at the same time I don't want to go down that line. But it helps. Vicious circle.

28/11

Well so far today I haven't cried. I lay awake crying quietly last night - staring out into the night. Feeling so alone. I wanted to call out for someone, but there wasn't really anyone I wanted to be with, and that intensified the isolation of me, that ache inside that said there's no-one for you ever and you have to somehow survive. At which point the option of suicide seemed a way out of this pain. An option to consider.

Cry From the Heart
Celia

Who will listen to cries ever silent?
Who dare ask
Words to touch
Chords of hidden begging soul?

Who will hold this disparate being
Never taught to care?
Battered, beaten neglected, touched
Reviled
Tortured black, deep despair.

Who are you
Who dare presume
The sorrow, pain, guilt?
You cannot –
For you fear
Touch will taint you too.

Whom amongst you
Dares to venture
Catacombs dank and dire?
Who will search, inquire
Learn, impart
Take my hand and lead me home?

Miscellaneous

My Struggle
Brita

Please don't tell me what's happening,
I don't understand,
Something's pulling me downwards:
Invisible hand.
In a strange dark world, looking for light,
Choose a direction, Left or Right;
Straining my mind, it becomes plain to see,
I can open some doors, but I need a key.
So where is this magical key to be found?
High in the sky, or deep underground?
I'll keep on struggling until I find,
The reason behind the birth of mankind.

The Egg I Live In
Dianne Aslett

The egg I live in
waits in shadow -
how long I've lingered
I can't say -

Its shell is crackable
I feel the sharp stings -
the all-too vivid light -
I hunch up my shoulders -
soothe my soul -

world within worlds
sisters' habits enthrall
Holy Grail -
wrap around me,
me, fermenting foetus -

I feel fragile -
glowing under moons -
nourished by darkness -
beyond the muffled sounds
the clocks can't stop.

Lost Soul
Celia

Who is She
Who takes to wander
Life's interminable seas.
A lost soul trying, trying hard
To cling to craggy shores.

As the sea changes
So does She
Without a moment's warning.
From calm to raging storm,
Waves crashing on jagged rocks.

Seafarers beware
For I think a siren's song She sings.
Luring those unwary folk
Who dare venture close.

So keep your distance
Save yourselves.

Don't put out to sea.
This storm must ride full out
This soul's not worth the price.

No Solace
Celia

A solitary road
I now must take.
No one to turn to
No one to trust.

You have condemned me
By your very words
The loneliest path
That man can tread.

My lips be sealed
Pain, angst, despair
Kept locked
Deep within my soul.

No hand extended
For final touch,
No one to share
My last goodbye.

Borderline
Dianne Aslett

My cherry coke
wobbles to the scribbles,

the cat swings manically
across the margin
my mother's demon eyes
pierce the red bottle,
reminding me unkindly
of how I came to be here,
fearing the searchlights.

Why? Because...
Ashman

You sit in the bar
Looking at me
As if I fell from the sky.
You're as tense as a spring,
Trying not to give in,
And unaccountably shy.
Oh you look cornered and trapped -
Well, how about that? -
But tell me, what can we do?
If you're asking me why
I'll say "It's only because
No one here knows me like you do."

If I rant at you then it's only because
No-one is talking to me,
And if I fall for you then it's only because
No-one is falling for me.
If I cry at night then it's only because,
I can't stand to sleep on my own,
And if I scream at you then it's only because,
I'm lost and I'm trying to get home.
If I ring you up then it's only because
I'm missing the way that we were,

And if you're second best then it's only because
I've always had a soft spot for her.
If I burn my fingers then it's only because
I've been playing with fire,
And if I tell the truth then it's only because
I've never been a very good liar.
And if I whisper to you then it's only because
You keep on listening to me,
And if I rattle my cage then it's only because
I've got a hunger to be free.
And if I smile at you then it's only because
You've got something that I need,
And if I scowl at you then it's only because
You've got the tools to make me bleed.
And if I slash and I burn then it's only because
I've got no reason to complain,
And if I rush straight in then it's only because
I need to prove I'll take the pain.
And if I wreck your place then it's only because
I'm terrified that you might forget
And if I stay in touch then it's only because
I'm not quite over you yet.
And if I make you cry then it's only because
I need to know that you can feel,
And if I'm good and behave then it's only because
I like to try to keep a deal.
And if I run away then it's only because
Running's a thing that I do,
And if I push too hard then it's only because
This one life must make up for two.
And if I beg and plead then it's only because
I always like to try and stay friends,
And if I want to stay friends then it's only because
I might be lonely at the end.

The Border
Ashman

Drifting down the border,
Just me, my guitars,
An assortment of stationery,
And too many books
That my ghosts never offer to carry.

From time to time another stranger
Will walk with me awhile
And offer to carry my books.
But always we part
Down perpendicular paths.

I pass lonely barbed-wire border posts
Guarding lands I'll never know
With their signs that forbid
Too many books,
Guitars and assortments of stationery.

Always along the border,
Never crossing:
With my guitars, too many books
And an assortment of stationery
That my ghosts never offer to carry.

Untitled
Anonymous

I know honey.
And your screams slice my skin
It's my blood too.

I know you can't see me.
Please don't believe me when I shout.
It's not you I see.

This woman isn't you.
You are not here, are not her.
I'm scared.

When it takes you, when you are lost
I'm lost too. I lose you too.
I'm scared.

1 in 10.
Please don't be special this time.
Come back baby, please.

Love you.

Go away and leave me alone
Elle Jay

I said it wrong, I messed it up
I tried but failed, alright?
So why replay on constant loop
And torture me all night?
I've lived it now a thousand times,
Each detail large or slight,
This unrelenting mocking din
Is making me feel shite.

Another Nail
Ashman

Today, this thought occurred to me:
What if this mind *doesn't* stop
When they finally drop me in a hole
And throw the dirt back over me?

She's gone...
Elle Jay

One long walk
One short pier
One dead laugh
One wet tear
One small pill
And fifty more
One long rope
And one big door
One last smile
And then she's gone
Come on, cruel world
Struggle on

Sound Advice for Social Occasions
Ashman

Keep secret your joy
And silently grieve,
Your heart should beat within your chest,
And not upon your sleeve.

Frustration
Elle Jay
Another day, another fight,
another urge, another plight,
another step, another pain,
another tear, another stain,
another cut, another scar,
another burn, another char,
another hate, another shame,
another wish, another blame,
another death, another birth,
another scream, another mirth,
another this, another that,
another lie, another fact,
another end that lies in sight,
another exit from this fight,
another chance for me to cry,
another chance to wonder why?
another day brings this along
another chance to hear life's song
another chance to want to die
another wish that I knew why
another life in wait for me
another time for me to be
another journey now to make
another chance to meet my fate

Late C20th Pet Hate Rant
Ashman

Old women on escalators
With tartan trolleys and purple rinses
Who STOP - not *quite* dead -
Whilst you peddle backwards

118

Treading escalator water.

Trains where the ringing of mobile phones
Remind me of work as I'm on my way home.

And talking of trains;
Non-smoking families with the nerve to complain
That they can't breathe, they're choking.
So why do they sit in the smoking carriage
When there's eight more coaches
For these holy non-smokers?

And talking of smoking;
Swan roll-up papers
with 'new improved glue'
That don't stick when you lick
Like they say that they do.

Smoke detectors sensitive to bacon
But deaf and dumb to conflagration.

Safety matches -
We all know the score,
Itemised phone bills -
Need I say more?

Rubbers that smudge,
Pencils that break,
Pens that don't write
But that flood and then scrape.
New fifty pences
And lighters that don't
And lovers who say
That they will then they won't.
CDs that jump
And answering machines

And the friends who run off
With the girls of my dreams.
But more than all these,
Though they all give me grief,
Is my want of direction
And lack of Belief.

Betrayed…
Elle Jay

A moment's words reduce me down to size
An altered view now seen through tangled lies
Once solid ground, once trusted, cracks and
                                        shakes
A newer me borne out of their "mistakes"
A million betrayals swimming round my mind
Perhaps it's true it's crueller to be kind?
A tall dark stranger stands in place of friend
The bubble's burst, the fiction's at an end
That mocking glare of knowing sears my soul
With hindsight. Is destroying me their goal?
I wish for freedom from doubt's murky throes
But no one has more power than he who knows
What other myst'ries lock me in suspense?
Much more amusement had at my expense?

All else is gone, but blackness still remains
Constricting, I find comfort in its chains
Too tempting to deceive and hide its snares
The blood-red pain of life, it always shares
No doubt defiles my trust in, or the shame
At knowing sadness treats me just the same
When all else fails there's still somewhere to turn
That stinging bite, I welcome its return.

A new day dawns and life's a different shade
Another complex game-move has been played
My house on sand destroyed by turn of tide
Condemned, once more, retreating back inside
I'd start again with first brick in the wall,
But at the bottom there's nowhere left to fall.

English Rose
Brita

You crawl up my wall
and invade my privacy
cockroach of the gutter
and life of depravity
Sometimes a red light
tells you to stop
pick up a calling card
in the phone box.
I slink through the alleyways
avoiding the law;
You love me, you loathe me;
You watch me in awe;
Bleeding lines
drawn with a knife,
I lick my wounds
this is life.
Money makes the world
go round.
Here's my flesh,
now take your pound.

Cracking the Code
Dianne Aslett

Before you emerged
out of the ether
Superman
was still anchored
amongst icicles
communing with his father,
and I laughed and cried
hysterically
crazy with grief
I scanned the skies
and clung to the earth
disabled by death wishes
choking dirt.

Before you,
a wild child
whimpered and giggled
in the trees
feral-like and foolish
fearing the searchlight
of human sight
I'd jump and dig
pulled and pulling,
shake, scream, complain
raking and breaking
taking roots to task
incandescent with rage
at another age,
at mother, my father.

But now, there's structure
to my insanity
my home smells sweet
with roses
and I can juggle
like a normal person.

How I Live Now
Naomi Salisbury

'How I Live Now' is the title of a book about a
society turned upside down, where normal
everyday life has been changed forever and people
are left fending for themselves individually on a day
to day basis. It seemed like a perfect title. I'm 24
years old, I work full time as a teacher, I live an
independent life and my ambitions are to be real
and to be safe.

I couldn't quite tell you when I fixed on those, but
unlike the rest of my life they seem to make some
sort of sense most of the time. In a perfect world all
of it would make sense all of the time, but I'm
learning to realise I might have to settle for a
slightly skewed version of perfect, or in fact a
completely back to front version. Where what I
hope for is the energy to make it through the day
even if it includes my entire range of emotions; the
energy to deal with the people I find so difficult and
frightening; the energy not to end up a wallowing
mass of self-pity, hiding from anything that might
help; the energy not to go for the short cut of self-
destruct. The energy to hide it all from the people

who aren't supposed to see me like this, to even know there's a problem. Sometimes I feel like it's all I can do to accept the limitations my emotions seem to place on me.

BUT, despite what I tell myself several times a day, there is no way this is going to beat me or stop me, broadly, doing what I want. Maybe I'll always have random mood swings, find it almost impossible to be in groups of people or believe that they want me there, lose my senses and perception and proportion without warning, be empty and bored and afraid of just being myself, maybe I'll end up back in hospital, but I'll still be here. A lot of the time that's how I live. On the wrong side of something somewhere.

Sometimes I feel like this splits me into two irreconcilable people; I feel like such a fraud just writing this, because today was OK. But being so divided means that even when the negative part has totally taken over, there's still a whisper there somewhere, still fighting it all. Maybe all the effort will only be to plug the gaps I feel like I'm full of, maybe not. I guess I'm still hanging in there, or maybe not.

What disappoints me the most is that I definitely can't have the one thing I'd like the most. The guarantee of a quiet life. I can't ever know what will set me off and what won't, so all I have is hope some days. Or maybe it's stubbornness or sheer bloodymindedness, but it's why I'm still here. I'm still hoping to be real and to be safe.

Sun
Donna Eaton

At dawn my sun would softly glow,
hope in life it came to show.
It warmed my world,
provided light,
until I was at rest at night.

Then one day it failed to rise,
the rays I knew lit not the skies.
My world had changed,
was not the same,
the sun replaced by dark and rain.

My darkness shows no path or road,
to guide me out, to offer light.
The gloom arrives with pain and fear,
and thoughts I do not wish to hear.

Other suns I see them shine,
but they do not extend to mine.
Their suns shine bright,
their worlds are warm.
What have I done to have mine torn?

Without my sun there is no dawn.
Those I love fade out, are gone
I sit alone, I pray to cry,
I only want to feel alive.

And, yet beyond my blinkered view,
there are others who have been here too.
Their suns extinguished,
their worlds were cold,
sad painful stories they have told.

But, now their worlds are light again,
warm sunrise came to soothe the pain.
They reached for help,
they found a way,
and this I must believe today.

I must find hope in what I'm told,
and struggle on to beat the cold.
One day, soon, I hope I'll see,
a glimmer of light,
a sun for me.

My Inner Child
Celia

Child of mine
Why do you treat me
In this torturous way?
Fill my mind, my every being
With emptiness and despair.

Inner child
Why can't you tell me
How you really feel?
Unburden, share answer, tell
Enable those to help.

Inner child
Why so scared?

Why can't you tell
And free yourself
And we be completely free?

Child of mine
Let me see
Through your eyes, as through mind.
Let me be alongside you
To share your hurt and pain.

Inner child
Why can't you see
That together we should have grown?
I know you need to be held
So that you can grow.

Child of mine
I wish I could take your hand,
Protect and help you grow.
I wish, sincerely wish
I didn't need it too.

Child of mine
I don't know where to find
The trust and love we need.
If only I could be with you
And lead us safely home.

Child of mine
I hope somewhere
Arms are waiting to embrace us all.
It's time to leave the prison cell
Step on the path
That may lead us home.

A Story of Growth
Overcoming a monster with the help of a quiet voice
Gail Silver

The negativity swallows me up when I'm not so good and then it behaves like a sponge drawing on negative thoughts past, present and future.

The sponge swells up and the associated feelings feed the negative thoughts. Then the pain starts. It spreads feeling worse than it really is in the life-threatening sense, and the sponge gets bigger.

Worst case scenarios form amongst the negative thoughts. Anxiety increases as does the pain. The monster which this has become creates inaccuracies of thought, and fear feeds on it all and the very fear itself.

There is no room for it to grow any more, but the monster does not know that. Neither does it care. It pushes into every nook and cranny expanding the spaces until I feel I will explode.

I can't cope with this any more!
The screaming starts inside my head. It gets louder and louder. It will not stop. It will not go away. I become more restless, more agitated, more anxious. I do not know what to do. Anger rises out of sheer frustration. The screaming inside my head gets louder still. It jangles my senses so I no longer hear, apart from the screaming. I no longer see because the way is barred by a wall the monster uses to surround me. I am numb, apart from the dreadful pain in my chest and the pounding in my head. It will not stop. How much longer must I

suffer this? Will it never stop? Will it never go away? Will I never be left in peace?

The monster that was a molehill has become a huge volcano that might erupt at any moment leaving inestimable damage in its wake.

Small everyday tasks and everyday problems swell into great catastrophes. Everything is beyond my control, including me.

I can't do anything right!

I am useless!

A waste of space!

Everything is against me!

Every ONE is against me!

NO one likes me!

I HATE MYSELF!

I WISH I WERE DEAD!!!!!!!!!!!!

A quiet gentle voice speaks to me. I look around. There is only me.

The quiet voice speaks to me from inside myself.

Yes. It will stop. It has stopped before. Remember?

A faint and distant memory.

The seed of a positive thought maybe?

The monster does not like this challenge. It struggles and writhes about trying to increase in size still further in an attempt to blot out the very idea that there is anything positive anywhere. Let alone for me!

Think.
You have done something positive today.
You got out of your bed this morning even though you did not want to. You washed and dressed too, and ate breakfast .

I did, didn't I?

That challenges your negative assumptions that you can't do anything right and that you are useless.

I suppose it does. (A hint of a smile appears despite myself. But it fades.)

You have challenged your negative thinking. Well done!

But every thing is against me!

Are you sure about that?

W..e...ll . Perhaps not everything. My pottery session went well yesterday. I was pleased with myself. My pieces turned out well.

Ah! So yesterday you experienced feeling good about your work?
Umm! Yes!

Some people liked my rock figure!
And when we had cleared up, the Director came in to ask the Arts Worker how the day had gone.

What made you mention that?

Oh, they said they liked having me there.

Really? Conclusions?

Er! Everyone isn't against me? And perhaps someone even likes me.

Do you still hate yourself

I suppose not. I have some good qualities, don't I?

Do you really need me to answer that?

No. It is a fact.

Anything else? Do you still want to be dead, for example?

I don't think so. (I reply guardedly)
I think that statement was more about how awful I felt and my inability to see how to manage or change things. In fact, the more powerful the helplessness, the more powerful the statements became.

A pause.

The mountain tumbles in on itself. The monster dies and the sponge dries up and withers away.

A realisation!

I have begun to challenge my faulty thinking patterns for myself!

Definition of a Non-smoker
Naomi Salisbury

A smoker who hasn't had a cigarette in five years.

This pretty much sums it up for me talking about self-destructive behaviour. I'm not saying you can't kick it, or that you can't kick it for good, but for me it's something that will always be lurking there in the background and I'll never be quite sure it's gone. In a way I'll want to know it's still there, that I still can, that the door isn't closed. And I know until I shake that feeling I'll never be able to let go, I'll always see a solution in a razor blade. I might be fighting with myself over it, but I still can't see it as a horrible thing to do, more a means to an end, a necessary evil, some kind of twisted security blanket. I wish I had the courage to leave it behind.

A Beautiful Goal

Mick Burke

The outside world,
A fearsome place,
The people, the sky,
The open space.

A friendly smile,
A wave, a nod,
Simple pleasures,
Yet so easily lost.

So nothing outside,
And cruelly ironic,
You look within,
And find there's no tonic.

So then at the bottom,
Take a deep breath,
Focus on the top,
'Cause there's nothing beneath.

Think of those pleasures,
You're going to regain,
Sweeter this time,
Because of past pain.

A worthwhile journey,
I have to insist,
And if I hadn't made it,
You couldn't read this.

From Victim of, to Victory over BPD

Sue Sanders

After 45 years of abuse of every kind, control by others and mental anguish, my life was not worth living and nothing, I firmly believed, would ever change. My life would forever consist of Borderline Personality Disorder (BPD), depression, psychotropic medication and daily self-harm, physical and mental disablement. I would never work again. That was my view and total conviction in January 2001.

Today I am in full-time employment, am getting fitter by the day - having lost 8 stones in weight - and am getting regular exercise. My depression is now reduced to 'mental flu' for which I need no medication. The self-harm is, on average, once every six months and the BPD is under control and in remission.

This is my story:

My parents blamed me for being born a girl and not being the second son they craved. For this I was punished with physical, emotional, psychological and sexual abuse by my father. My mother knew about this but did nothing. My older brother also sexually abused me. I wet the bed till I was 11 years old but my parents did nothing about this – and they were teachers!

Mistreatment was a 'normal' part of my life. My first abuse by a stranger was when I was five when he 'rescued' me from being molested by another stranger and then raped me. The pain and fear he instilled in me and his threat to return and do the same made me keep this secret for 43 years. From the age of five to 14, I was abused by strangers and other children on at least 15 other occasions. None, though, was as severe as the first.

From the age of five, my weight increased massively. The heaviest I have been was 30 stones. At 18, I twice had my jaws wired, and eventually had my stomach stapled. All was in vain. I took my first overdose when I was 14 – slimming tablets. I guess that was my first depression.

At 16, I started a career in nursing people with learning disabilities. My time off duty was completely ruled by my father. I was his slave. My orders were to fill my spare time with heavy labour and house repairs. At this time, I was 30 – I'd been a ward manager for seven years. Yet I remained convinced that if I failed to do as he ordered, I would be expelled from the family for ever. If I didn't have my family, abusive as it was, I had nothing. I'd already learnt that negative attention is better than no attention.

A year later, I was admitted to a psychiatric hospital. I was suicidal, self-harming and drinking heavily. On my first weekend leave I was greeted home by my father saying: "The garden fence needs fixing". I took another overdose on my return to the hospital.

I survived. They sent me to a psychotherapy group, and there I met the man who three years later became my husband. They also told me I had a personality disorder. But, with no information about what this meant, or any specific diagnosis, I rejected the notion completely.

During the next 14 years I went into hospital 16 times and was angry at the world. Initially the marriage was wonderful, but then my husband took over from my father, in the total control of my life. He had an affair with my best friend and his control was such that when we went on holiday they shared a bed and I slept alone. By this time both my parents had died. My mother died from cancer and my father, six months later, from old age.

Having now lost my nursing career, I became a permanent psychiatric patient, taking enough medication to stop a rhinoceros. I became an extremely vocal and argumentative service user. As chairperson of a user-led forum, I continued being 'challenging', so they invited me to help plan a new psychiatric hospital by passing on service user views on services, policies and facilities. Together we did some excellent work and this new hospital opened in 2000.

By now my husband's affair was in full fling. I was self-harming daily, drinking heavily and weighed about 29 stones. I had to go into hospital again but was very scared - my reputation preceded me. Rightly or wrongly, nursing staff were made aware of the fact I could be difficult, and would complain at the drop of a hat. I was described by a senior nurse manager as:

Sue was, quite frankly, the worst patient to have on your ward. She would scare the staff with her frustratingly illogical arguments and unreasonable demands.

She would cause quiet dissent with other like-minded patients and consistently battle against the system, coercing it to take responsibility for her and then using that as a lever to 'prove' she was an ultimate victim of that same system.

Every ward manager's nightmare!

Far from treating me differently from other patients these staff were the first to show me the consequences of my actions. If I pestered, they withdrew. If I self-harmed I would have to approach them, not them approach me. I learned trust. Finally, instead of just treating my depression, they started looking at my personality disorder, and supported me in accepting the diagnosis. Of the nine criteria for Borderline Personality Disorder, I recognised eight of them within myself.

Support continued. They suggested I go into Main House Therapeutic community for a year. This was a specialist residential community which used group therapy, 24 hours a day, to treat, predominantly, Borderline Personality Disorder. At that time, the rule was you had to be free of psychotropic medication to be admitted there. So this meant giving up the medication and safety of the hospital – and I was psychologically addicted to both. The deciding factor was the blackmail from my husband. Go in or we get divorced!

In May 2001 I went into Main House, a physically disabled psychiatric patient who was unemployable and had nothing to live for. I was to spend a year away from home and the people I knew and go to a place where there were rules and boundaries for everything, and all this with no medication. I was terrified.

Now it was my turn to be challenged, by staff and other residents. Everything I said or did was analysed, dissected and discussed by the community. For the first four months I did little to change myself. On the other hand, I had started to learn that abuse was *far* from 'normal' and that I had choices.

Whilst there I also realised I'd swapped a controlling father for a controlling husband. I learned the consequences of my actions and the effects my behaviours had on others. I realised that much of my anger was concealing hurt and fear. My lack of maternal instinct and dislike of all children was actually fear. Fear of play and fear that I would abuse children as my father had done. Being obese and showing pseudo-confidence I was horrified to learn that other residents felt intimidated by me. So I had to look at the way I spoke, my body language, my whole demeanour. I started to look at myself minutely; I had always been a victim but did not have to continue as a victim. I gained an insight into my past self that was terrifying as well as embarrassing. The whole experience was the worst thing I'd ever been through but the best thing I'd ever done. I think the most important thing I learned was that no matter how much support I got, no matter who I talked to or what their ideas were, the only person who could make me change…was me!

On leaving Main House I approached, cap in hand, the director of nursing back at the trust I'd been so vocal in previously. I asked if there were any committees, I'd previously been on in the planning stages of the hospital, which I could re-join. An emphatic 'No' was followed by a job offer. The director of Nursing asked me to be Assistant Co-ordinator in the Care Programme Approach (CPA) and to audit and teach CPA throughout the trust. This was the biggest boost to my confidence I've ever had. If he and others believed in me, perhaps it was time I believed in myself.

That was back in 2002. Since then, I have divorced my husband and taken full responsibility for myself in all aspects of my life. My former carers within the trust now fully accept me as a colleague, with any previous reputation now fully dispelled. My insight to myself continued to grow and develop, even though it scares me sometimes.

It has not been a bed of roses, since learning to live alone, but I enjoy my life, knowing it is *my life* and no one else controls it. The depression comes and goes – as it did last year, with a vengeance – but I accept that I cannot control it but I can control my own behaviours. I don't know what the future holds, but whether good or bad, it's my future to make.

I know I have achieved a tremendous amount in the past four years and hope I will continue to do so, though I do have great difficulty in hearing compliments or comments about these achievements. I also have arguments about the force behind these achievements, as I have said it was fear which drove me, while others say it was bravery. The biggest force I have now is me, and I'm a person I now like and am happy to be.

I'll leave the last words for the nurse manager who said I was a nightmare. His comments about the 'new' me are these:

Sue has been 'reborn' into the person that many of us saw hidden away for all those years. Having made and undertaken some mammoth life decisions, Sue is possibly one of the bravest and most reflective people I know. How many of us look in the mirror and absolutely accept the person you see before you? How many of you actually criticise yourselves, your behaviours and then do something about what you find? Sue has, and does. That is her strength and makes her the person she is today.

X...
Depressive, BPD and happy!

Where Am I? The Conclusion
Sue Sanders

Where Am I?
Somewhere in a dark room inside my mind
Is a tightly closed door which I hide behind
Although I have searched, I cannot yet see
The door to the room which hides the real me.

Inside the darkness I scream and I shout
For someone to help me, to please let me out
I feel my thought processes have been abused
And the thoughts that remain are all so confused.

I honestly don't know just why they all bother

To say do this, do that, do the other
For the body they talk to, it does not care
Because the 'controller', me, is not there.

My feelings of confidence have now all gone
In this state of mind I cannot go on
You can't call this living. You can't call this life
It's just an existence, one that's full of strife.

When will it be over, when will it end
Will I always be broken, or will I mend
To be well again, they say I'll achieve it
Only when that occurs, only then I'll believe it.

As I search in the dark recesses inside my mind
Hating and fearing all that I find
Confusion and terror are all that I see
As I search in the darkness looking for me.

I Am Here
So many doors were there for protection
The reason for why would take some detection
The search is now over, all doors now unlocked
Thoughts and emotions all free and unblocked.

I no longer shout, but I quietly ask
For help and support whilst I complete this task
I'm now moving forwards, away from the past
Although sometimes stumbling, this movement will
last.

So many questions, so many words
So many times I thought they weren't heard
But they were listening, I could not see
The person not listening? That person was me.

Self reliance emergent and growing in might
I now look at life with increasing delight
Though I'm not sure when this new life begun
I've learned to enjoy it; I've learnt to have fun.

Responsibility in me has grown
Who looks after me? That work is my own.
Achievements are many, which bring much relief
The future is mine, I now have that belief.

I looked in the room through terror and fright
But it's no longer dark, but sunny and bright
Confusion and terror, from them I am free
As I live in the brightness, happy as me.

Elsewhere
Ashman

London. Euston to be precise, a few streets away
from the railway station and the newly completed
British Library. It's February 1998 I think, or it could
be '97 – it makes little difference if I can't recall the
year. But I know it was February: it always is.

She's trying to tie a pair of my dirty socks around
my wrists to stop the bleeding. It's late evening and
my limbs are shaking uncontrollably though not with
the piercing cold of this winter's night. I'm standing
here, in this quiet street, with my arms held out like
some Victorian schoolchild waiting for the cutting
blow of a cane, whilst she fumbles with cold and
clumsy fingers. My weekend bag sits at my feet
looking as crumpled as I feel, and my eyes smart
from the too many tears that have been shed.
From somewhere far away I hear her voice, a

cocktail of anger, fear and frustration that mouths the words "casualty" and "A and E".

The Stanley knife is still in my hand and still I'm struggling to catch my breath between convulsive sobs. Every cell in my body still screams out "NO!" I can feel my brain smashing itself against the inside of my skull, like the football I used to kick against the garden fence when I was more of a boy. And my heart feels like it has been dropped in to a bucket of rusty nails and acid.

From somewhere inside, deeply barricaded behind cotton wool and alcohol, I look out at the scene that my eyes are passing to me in a series of blurred images and I find it farcical.

Blade in hand and socks on wrists and blood on socks and socks on feet. I manage to get a message through to my mouth. It moves, forms words, then I can hear my voice all broken and cracked.

"Fuck A and E. Where's the nearest pub?"

Don't get lost in this maze of confusion. There is elsewhere.

February 2000. This time I'm sure of the year. I remember the mini-festival we threw to mark the beginning of the new Millennium – or the end of the old one. And I know it was February – it always is.

West Cumbria, and it's cold. I can't get in to the house. For the first time, she's locked the door.

She's locked the door that is never locked but always left on the latch that we can both reach, with our tiny wrists, through the letter box. Tonight, the mortice has been turned with all the finality of a portcullis slamming in my face. She might as well have painted "NO" across the door in fuck-off two foot high letters.

I'm in the back yard. No blades (they took them off me), no socks on wrists, just the dirty echo of where, half an hour ago, the handcuffs were. But every cell is screaming. Football brain. And in my veins, an angry cocktail of hot blood, diazepam, whiskey and paracetamol that hasn't yet floored me. I need to be inside, I need to be safe, I need it all to stop. I need a "YES".

From inside a bunker lined with cotton wool and fear, I hear the sound of breaking glass as my undeniable boot makes contact with the lower pane of the back door.

But don't get too lost in this maze of confusion. There is elsewhere.

July, that same year. But it feels like February. The rain is coming down in horizontal waves, so hard that it sounds like some primeaval hand is throwing gravel at the side of the caravan. On the stereo, Thom Yorke is telling me that I'm just like my Dad, and for all I know, he might be right. Somewhere beyond the rain and behind the night is the Lake District. Inside the caravan there's just me, Thom, a lot of blood and six outrageously large police officers.

The nearest one has got a beard. My eyes might feel like they've been sand blasted, but I can still see his beard. His feet touch the floor and his helmet scrapes across the ceiling. Behind him is another policeman. Behind that policeman, is a policewoman and another fucking policeman. And there are two more, half inside and half outside. Wall to wall and floor to ceiling coppers. Behind cotton wool and Radiohead parapets, some part of me struggles to formulate the joke that I know is in here somewhere.

I'm having a row with the beard. About A and E, about how badly I'm bleeding, about first aid certificates - Jesus Christ, we're comparing first aid certificates! He's telling me how depressing Thom Yorke is and I'm telling him how crap beards are. And all the time they are trying to get me to step outside. Little do they know that I've been in too many tricky situations in pubs to know that you should never step outside.

Don't get too lost in this maze of confusion. They say there is elsewhere.

London. June 8th 2004. It's hot and I'm sweating buckets in a tie and shirt, trousers and jacket. I'm looking at my hands and they're shaking – well, wouldn't you? This is the headquarters of the Department of Health. If you get up and stroll across the room and look out of the enormous windows you'll see the Cenotaph and just beyond that Downing Street. It doesn't look very real.

At the lectern in front of me, the Minister of State for Health is giving a speech to this gathering of clinicians, experts in Personality Disorder and service users. I'm far too frightened and anxious for anything she's saying to go in. In a moment, she'll finish and then I'll have to stand up and deliver my speech, and I'm counting on the fact that when I get out of this chair I'll dissociate and become a different Dale. And if that doesn't happen, then the ground better sure as hell open up and swallow me.

This might be another part of the maze but it still doesn't feel much like elsewhere.

April 2005. Carleton Clinic, Carlisle. It's a lovely spring evening, though the sound of the M6 is disturbing the tranquillity of the place. Fran and I are leaning against the wall of the training building desperately trying to put our heads back together and drawing frantically on our cigarettes as if they're full of the emotional superglue we need.

We've just spent the last hour and a half trying to describe to students on a Personality Disorder course what it feels like to be Borderline. What emptiness feels like; how the fear of abandonment can rule over your life with an invisible and all pervasive presence; why self-harm and suicide are always an option. From up here you can look down on the maze and you can see it stretching and twisting away in all directions, from horizon to horizon, as far as the mind's eye can see.

The students leave, offering us a few words of thanks as they pass, and make their way laughing and chatting across the sun reflecting car park. We watch them get in to their cars and head off for elsewhere. I get the distinct impression that they know where it is, but just aren't telling.

As a thousand disturbed memories crash around in my football brain, it occurs to me that I may be lost.

On a scorching day in June 2005 I find myself sitting on the grass outside the Fairnington Centre in Hexham, rocking backwards and forwards and talking to myself. I didn't get to bed last night, didn't take my meds and drank glass after glass of red wine until 6am. I've spent the last fifty minutes falling apart in my shrink's office. I'm not sure what it's achieved, but I know one thing for sure: I'm lost.

I don't seem to be able to get up and I know I can't drive home. For no apparent reason I suddenly find myself making a daisy chain. My God, "the lunatic is on the grass", and in a Basil Brush t-shirt. There's a joke in here somewhere. Boom-boom.

Then, as my shaking hands struggle with uncooperative daisies, a memory slowly forms like mist gathering on water on a summer's evening. A memory of another June day, sitting outside my tent in a field in Loweswater, at a time when I was homeless, moneyless, jobless and careless. "Less is more" they say, and at that time I felt more at peace and more familiar than at any time since I was a child. During that peculiar summer, something deep and forgotten within me stirred; another part of me that was whole, integrated, and

147

content but that like a frightened child had been hiding whilst the chaos raged outside.

Suddenly, all is clear. I know where Elsewhere is. I've been there before and I remember what it feels like. More than that, I know that there is nothing more important in my life than getting there again. The choice is a stark and simple one: get to Elsewhere or forever remain lost.

If you're lost in a maze of confusion, and you've wandered amongst towering hedges for so many years that you no longer have any sense of direction; when all hope seems to have gone and you're close to exhaustion: there are only two things you need to escape – a straight line and a chainsaw. Dig deep and you may find that you've been carrying those things with you all the time as you wandered. Then all you need is the courage and the strength to pull the starter cord.

Too many people make the mistake of defining and conceptualising Recovery in socio-economic terms. Can you work and keep a job? Maintain a relationship? Function without too much assistance in the society and culture that the accident of your birth has placed you in? Can you pay your taxes? Well that's all bullshit, baby.

Define your own Recovery.

Find Elsewhere.

Note: Inspired by a quote from Debbie McNamara: "Don't get too lost in this wave of confusion – there is elsewhere."

Why My Diagnosis is a Good Thing

Fenella Lemonsky

I am grateful to my diagnosis of BPD as until I saw my psychiatrist who specialises in it I was under a few psychiatrists who were good but didn't know what to do to help me.

I was very ill and went from crisis to crisis, but getting to my new psychiatrist after 15 years of chaos, trauma and rollercoaster emotional living I met someone who understood me, what it was like for me and who was there for me with a very good specialist team.

I was encouraged to find safe boundaries and work closely in the specialist psychotherapy day unit and help build a bit of self esteem and to maintain normal non-chaotic and stormy relationships.

Learning that every time someone close went away they weren't abandoning me, just going away on holiday or something.

Learning that I didn't have to use my self destructive behaviours to get something.

Learning self respect, trust and safety as well as containment.

Learning that life may be a piece of shit but it does get better and slowly but surely.

Learning that the answers are not in a bottle of pills.

Learning that interpersonal relationships are very painful and need to be treated with kid gloves.

Learning a new found respect for the team and those close to me.

Learning boundaries. Saying 'No' when it felt ok-to myself and others- without eating myself up about it in many ways.

Learning to assert myself without aggression.

Learning that I have needs and getting a focus on how those needs are going to be met without depending on others to make it happen.

Learning that just because I am having a bad day- the world is not coming to an end - just Fen is having a very rotten rough day and night and tomorrow is a whole new day to look forward to-and planning for it.

Learning that as those abuse me I can physically and emotionally distance myself.

Learning that when my GP is busy it means he has other patients and NOT that he is not interested.

Learning that despite all the crap around me, I have come through a tough one and should feel jolly proud of myself and the team who helped get me there.

V-BPD Day (But Only A Day)

Ashman

Proclaim it on the Pathe News
And on the BBC,
Today has been a day for us
Of glorious Victory!

Today we polished up our teeth
And ate up all our beans;
Never made a peak rate call
But lived within our means.

Today we didn't turn to drink,
We're AWOL from the pub;
Today we did the washing up
And other things we should.

Today we watched the sun go down,
But not from in our bed;
We balanced up our finances
And baked some splendid bread.

Today we didn't slash our wrists
Or overdose on pills;
Today we didn't call you up
And curse you for our ills.

Proclaim today for what it is,
For all the world to see:
Today has been a day for us
Of glorious Victory!

Coming to Terms, Making Changes, Moving On
Gail Silver

It really is ridiculous! Here am I at 55 years of age, and I'm struggling to say how I got here. I can write. I've been through my own personal hell and back, but how have I done it? What were the key issues? What have I learnt? How have I changed? I manage to get through life these days but how do I do it and ... well ... how have I learnt to do it?

Oh! This is infuriating!

The trouble is, I have spent such a lot of years not being able to talk at all about any of my difficulties, and now I can talk (and write) about all the negativity which has taken several more years, but I'm not very good at talking (or writing) in a positive way about myself or the changes I have been able to make.

OK. Let's look at the beginning. Well, I guess it's the middle really. Isn't that where the usual turning point is?

****

It is 1992, towards the end of the year, I find myself in hospital. I'm no longer looking after myself. I won't eat. I won't drink. I won't talk. Even if I could, I don't know what to say. Even if I knew what to say, I don't know how to say it.

The bottom has dropped out of my world. I can't carry on anymore. I am in a deep, deep hole. It is so deep that I don't see light at all. In fact, before that, I went down a long dark tunnel where I felt totally disorientated by the twists and turns of my life. So here I am, lying in a bed face to the wall, literally. I hurt. I'm lost. I am utterly alone. I hurt oh so much! But, **DON'T YOU TOUCH ME**! And, **DON'T YOU TALK TO ME EITHER**! I do not exist.

Every week there is a review. Every week there is no change. I sit there like a block of wood, and when it ends I am back in bed facing the wall. Nothing exists.

Then one day the Registrar calls me to an interview room. He says I can say what I like. I say nothing. I just sit. This goes on, once a week, for about an hour. There are long silences. Sometimes, he asks me how I'm feeling.

How I'm Feeling? I shout in my head. **How I'm feeling? What DOES he mean? Just let me go!** *I don't feel anything. Just leave me be.*

"You seem very angry."

"Are you angry with me?"

Angry! Angry! Me? I'm not angry! I'm not angry at all! *Why should I be angry?*

"No," I whisper. There is an absolute rage going on inside my head: a never-ending bloodcurdling scream. But I cannot see it for what it is.

What goes on here is someone giving ME time. Someone interested in ME, and wanting to help ME. No one has been for ME before.

This Registrar goes up on the old pedestal!! HE is going to sort out all this mess and muddle AND make me all better!

Well, actually he is not. He hasn't got that magic pill or that magic wand I <u>so</u> want him to have. What he has got is the ability to help me begin to understand what is going on for me and the patience while I struggle to talk.

I have got something too. The beginnings of a realization that some people can be trusted not to hurt me physically or verbally; to stab me in the back when I thought they were my friend; to desert me as they always seem to have done in my past. There is no 'playing games' here. Just plain honesty! This is something new, and I will always remember this as the very start of my journey of change.

****

Some years later, I am in hospital yet again. In the intervening period, I have had group therapy, art therapy, been to an eating disorder unit, had family therapy, and am currently involved in couple therapy.

I started with severe depression and bipolar affective disorder (manic depression), though the latter does not seem right.

It's review day. Will I be able to ask what the matter is? It will be questioning authority! Will I <u>dare</u>?

Anyway, 'they' haven't told me the truth! Something is going on here, and I want to know <u>exactly</u> what it is! Um! Will 'they' tell me? Am I able to ask?!

"Can you come for your review please?"

I go in the room. I sit on a chair. Can I ask?
The Consultant is talking. I answer the usual questions but I'm not really paying attention.
Will I ask? Or won't I?

"Is there anything you want to say?" the Consultant asks me.

Ah! My cue! Can I take it? <u>Yes!</u>

"Er... Will you please tell me what you see my diagnosis as?" I ask.

"It's not important for you to know that." The Consultant replies.

Oh yes it is! I yell in my head. *How <u>dare</u> you not tell me!*

"I don't think labels are helpful." The Consultant continues.

Argh!!!!! "Yes, but I want to know what you think". I can't believe I didn't yell that out!

"Why do you want to know?"

I'm stunned into silence. I wasn't prepared for that. I was just expecting a simple answer to a simple question.

"I want you to go away and think about why you want to know."

I leave the room, fuming! *How dare you talk to me like that! How dare you not answer my question!*

I haven't been in my room more than five seconds before I know all my answers to that question! But I have to wait a week.

****

Right!

"I want to know what my diagnosis is so I can come to understand it. If I can understand it, I can see how it affects me. If I understand that, then I can change what I can change, and learn to live with what I can't. I can't do any of this if you don't tell me what my diagnosis is."

"Borderline personality disorder."

"Thank you!" I leave the room and return to mine. Um! Fine! I know the diagnosis alright. Er... But, what is it?

I ask the Nurse for any literature on the subject. She comes back later with a short piece she has. On reading the nine criteria included therein, the diagnosis seems to fit like a glove. I feel like I have come in from the cold! I need to know more!

I ask for any available literature or book titles suitable to my needs. I have no time to read through weighty professional tomes.

For whatever reason, the information is not forthcoming. *'They've' forgotten me! 'They' don't want to help me! I'm being ignored! How <u>dare</u> you!*

Next review, I ask again. Not quite 'nothing', I suppose, as I am told by a Registrar not to look on the Internet, "It's full of rubbish."

Fine! For once in my life, I actually do as I am told. I really don't want rubbish, I want facts.

Almost a year goes by, and I still have nothing but a diagnosis. It is difficult to keep asking over and over because I mustn't be a nuisance. I mustn't question authority. Doing either (or both!), means I am a very bad person.

Blow it! I've got a computer now. I'm <u>going</u> to look on the Internet!

Oh dear!

"Borderline personality disorder is not a mental illness…"

Oh! So I'm not ill then. That means I must be telling lies.

"Borderline personality disorder is biological… is genetic… is environmental…"

Make up your minds!

"Borderline personality disorder cannot be cured… cannot be treated…"

Oh! So there is no hope for me then.
Ah, but wait a minute...

"It fades with age..."

It's a young adult's disorder then! *So __why__ have I got this to deal with in my fifties!*

"People with this diagnosis are manipulative... attention-seeking... demanding... aggressive... time-wasters... argumentative... Do not improve with hospitalization... Will not stay on therapy programmes..."

Oh dear, oh dear, oh dear! I really <u>am</u> a waste of space. 'They' won't bother helping me then! I shall be a drain on services and staff.

I re-visit websites. I look at message boards. I read summaries and abstracts on studies... experiments... on various studies. I'm wary of the latter. I know these can be biased, and outcomes manipulated according to who is funding them, and so on. I have at last managed to find one or two books on the subject. Sadly, the vast majority are American.

Aren't there any British books on the subject? Aren't there any UK based message boards? Isn't there <u>anything</u> positive, instructive or helpful anywhere?

Ah! Perhaps that Registrar was right after all. No! I don't believe it! It can't <u>all</u> be rubbish! I so want to prove him wrong.

I keep looking. I rediscover some of the sites I have already seen. (Being computer literate would have helped. I wouldn't have to keep starting from scratch if I'd known about 'bookmarks'!)

Someone's written a series of articles; personal perspectives and experiences, intuitive thoughts. This is more like it.   Gracious! A UK site! Borderline UK... and a BUK message board!

I've been in such a tearing hurry to find the answer... the magic wand... the cure... that I have picked up on, and seen only all the negative stuff. Well, I'm expert at that, and as a consequence have unfortunately been 'primed' by that Registrar's remark! *He was wrong! Blasted doctors! 'They' are as bad as everybody else. 'They' don't want to help me at all. 'They' are all against me.*

****

It's 2001. I join the Borderline UK group.   The people on the message board know what it's like. They know the pain. For many, the experiences are worse than mine. For some, they are less so. However, here everyone is allowed to have their say... to be angry and vent it... to be in pain and scream about it... to feel so desperately alone and say so. Everyone feels supported in the sharing, and acknowledged as the person he or she really is.

People say what helps and what doesn't. They talk of how they get through the day, hour, or minute. They tell each other, "you are not alone with this any more" and ... "we are here for you".

I am here now. I can talk. I can listen and am heard, and I acknowledge this realization. It's safe. I do not feel threatened. Skills acquired during the various therapies help me with this. I belong somewhere at last.

We swap experiences, book titles, articles, websites... that we have found helpful. There is such anger and pain here, but there is lots of laughter too.

We challenge our faulty thinking patterns, we express our feelings, we say what hurts and sometimes why. We are allowed to be as we are.

****

Historically, borderline personality disorder has been given a seriously bad press. The diagnosis has been a bad 'label' to have since once you have it you can not loose it or have it changed. It has very much been a diagnosis of exclusion.

Things are changing for the better in some places, but sadly not in others. For those with this disorder things cannot change quickly enough.

I do not consider my diagnosis as a 'label'. For me it has been, and always will be, a tool. In fact, for me, it's the key to unlocking my problems and being able to solve some of them.

****

I recognise that I have problems. I know why I have them. Somebody else 'did' this to me. 'They' have locked me into this way of development which has left me inadequately prepared for living in the real world as a fully functioning and emotional adult. I know, and accept, that my 'somebody-elses' are in part, the product of their own upbringing and period in history. Not as an excuse to excuse them for their actions, but rather that I understand why 'they' behaved thus. That was the creation of my problems, but they are mine, and I own them as such.

I acknowledge that I am extremely angry. However, I have learnt how to allow myself to feel all that anger, that inner rage and accompanying hurt, and put it where it belongs rather than take it out on myself or others who had nothing to do with it. I still have some to sort out, when the time is right. In the meantime I hold it safe and do not let it leak, if I can help it.

I am still learning to nurture my own self; to hold ME while I hurt, grieve for what I lost, and what I never had.

I have learnt how to challenge my erroneous thinking patterns and my automatic thought responses, the result of which may have been inappropriate behaviours.

This means I no longer put my perceived 'good fairies' on those high pedestals and then knock them off just as quickly when they commit some perceived sin where they become the 'wicked witches'. People are not all wonderful, or all bad and nasty. They are a mixture of both good and bad, and various degrees of each in between. Therefore, I no longer think of mental health professionals (particularly doctors) as the bad 'them' who are to be challenged, contradicted and fought at <u>every</u> turn on <u>every</u> issue at <u>every</u> opportunity. I do not have to 'do as I am told', which had also been the way I had viewed such authority figures when they spoke to me. Oh such problems I had with authority figures!

I now allow myself to disagree; I enter more into a dialogue on the current issue, and I have not got this 'perfect' either, but that's OK. I still doubt, feel that it's wrong, but I know I am allowed to respond in this way rather than as a small child to a parent. I AM an adult after all. I have trouble quite 'believing' it yet, but I 'know' it.

There are other life experiences that are not all black or white and nothing in between. For example, I don't have to feel unwell all the time. Yes, I have unwell periods but I have well periods too and various 'greys' in between. Light is not all absorbed (black) or all reflected (white) either. Neither is it just grey in between. Put light through a prism and it splits into a rainbow of colours and that is how my life can be too. Good gracious! Did I REALLY just write that? That's a positive statement if ever there was one. What has happened to that total negativity I used to be surrounded with?

What else does this mean for me? Well, if my husband goes out, on good days (and there are a lot more of them now) he has not gone for ever, he is going to come back after a period of time and while he is away I can be with myself. I don't like it when he goes, but I can be realistic about it. After all, he can't be there all the time – and he doesn't need to be. He does have a life of his own to engage with as well as being with me

Sometimes, on really bad days when he went out (or just left the room!) he didn't just 'abandon' me and was never coming back, he ceased to have existed at all!

It's 2005 now and this does still happen to a degree, when I am not so good and though I don't believe it I do know he will be coming back. Rationalization of my thought processing in this way is commonly becoming as automatic as the initial negative thought itself and belief is following more as time goes by.

All this and lots more besides, has been accomplished by discovering a sheer strength and determination that I never knew I had, or was possible, enabling me to find out about borderline personality disorder and myself, and allowing me to change my thinking and self-damaging behaviours.

I have learnt how to talk, to feel, and to talk some more. I have learnt how to recognise how I feel, what I feel and to describe the feelings and why they are there. I have learnt how to 'feel' these feelings and emotions, allow myself to do so, and nurture myself during the process.

I have learnt to challenge my negative thinking, discover why I do it and look for alternatives. In this way I can recognise that when another person is grumpy, moody or angry it may not be because of who I am, or what I did or said, but rather something arising from somewhere else entirely and therefore not my responsibility. This means I can bypass the feeling bad about myself or that it was my fault.

When it is me who is feeling grumpy, moody or angry, I can recognise why and where it stems from (most of the time) and therefore I avoid putting blame where it does not belong.

I couldn't have got to where I am today without a great deal of hard work and practise. Without the encouragement, support, guidance, and a great deal of patience and understanding, and ...er... challenges given to me by doctors, nurses, therapists from various fields, friends, family, arts related therapy with Creative Response, local Mental Health Line, and last but by no means least Borderline UK none of it would have been possible.

To all I offer my sincere gratitude.

I still fall into that deep black hole, familiar to so many of us, from time to time. Thankfully, though, I can scramble up the ladder I could never find in the blackness, with a fair bit of speed or walk round the hole in the first place. Sometimes, I even manage to avoid the street it's in!

I am under no illusion that I am at the end of my journey. I have some way yet to travel. I am determined to press on with the changes that may be necessary and the challenges I may still have to face.

Memories are less distorted and I can see things much clearer these days. Feelings I appropriately express. Like my anger which does not roll on and on as an ever increasing snowball tumbling down hill getting bigger and bigger sucking in every past, present and future hurt and rage. It's more proportional to the incident that sparked it off.

I will remind myself when the day seems grey and is getting darker that it will not last and that I might have to go with it, just for a while. Like those days when my mood is very low and I feel as if I am tumbling into that black hole again. I know my mood will lift eventually and it does not take as long as I expected. I try my best to keep positive despite it all by thinking of any positive things I have done or else do something positive. It does not have to be anything too big.

So there really is light at the end of the tunnel. We need to do our best to keep pressing forward with our eyes wide open, practising what we have learned from each other and the professionals.

Good luck and best wishes to us all!

A letter from beyond
Elle Jay

You never knew the depths I sank to, you didn't know me then. Even talking about it now I manage to be flippant and add in feelings I'm sure weren't there at the time. The fear, despair, pain, and death wish become unwitting companions to humour and hope. My own words surprise me and I'm convinced I'm talking about someone else. I suppose I am. It always sounds less severe than maybe it ever was. But who knows, I made it, perhaps it never was that bad. I often ask myself in those moments of idle thought when the world's rushing by the windows and I'm on autopilot, have I betrayed her and the pain she felt? What did I lose to gain myself? I think the answers are no and nothing, but I'm not always sure.

As I gently stroke your stomach and catch sight of the war torn state of my naked body curled around you, I often wonder how you piece it all together. The me I was and the me I am. What do you make of the scars? Do they still speak the message they were designed to convey? Or do they seem misguided, erratic and crazy? A reflection of some dangerous depth that lurks in my character or the track marks of a beast long since exorcised. I know you would only tell me what you truly thought if you knew it wouldn't hurt me. Your silence intrigues me.

Sometimes I think you're lucky because you can look with curiosity devoid of guilt. Those who knew me throughout that time can never be so confident that they didn't play at least some small part. If they were ever brave enough to voice their worries, I'd say, "Pick one of the small ones if you have to". The vengeance that filled me gave way to a kind of serenity and I'd much rather tell people what they want to hear. I stopped assigning blame and transferred my assets from the past to the present. It's a sounder investment.

But to the outside observer the legacy of pain scarred all over still needs an owner.

Perhaps I should sell the rights on e-Bay.

The other thing you make me think is how would I describe this journey if you ever wanted to hear it in full? Maybe I'd be all shy and mysterious to keep you interested. Maybe I'd dig out the reams and reams of diaries, poems and stories that this pain created and watch anxiously as you flicked through them. Or maybe I'd tell the truth – I was lost in my own internal hell and after a decade of failed discovery attempts during which I encountered every flavour of mental health professional and tasted every colour of capsule available I stumbled on a small nectar-filled flower that captured my attention. He never threatened me with recovery, he just asked me why it was so scary. He appealed to my scientific nature and gently encouraged me to test the things I'd assumed were true. And ultimately that was all there was to it.

So if I had to tell you the things I learned, I'd put it like this: I learned that as I look into your eyes I can think about how good it feels and how good it has felt in the past, and not about how I will survive when you leave. I learned that despair is the worst feeling in the world, but it always passes. I learned that even islands can be submerged by the tide and the more links you have to the mainland the easier it is to escape when you feel the water rising. I learned that trusting you is possible and more fun than distrusting you. I learned that my past is always part of me and some parts are harder to forget than others, but that the present is most of who I am. I learned that the world looks gorgeous when the sun shines and laughter dissipates tension but violence escalates it. I learned that time and patience are the same thing – things that take a long time take a lot of patience. I learned that all of this sounds hollow to someone with no hope, but I also learned that where there is life there is hope.

Of course I couldn't avoid the classics, like the realisation that life has no guarantees and that recovery is more about constant maintenance than any steadfast distinction between a state of being ill and a state of being well. I don't *assume* this will last forever. I don't *assume* we'll last forever. It's better to work to increase the probabilities than leave it to chance anyway.

Most of all I learned there is another way to be, a gentler way to be, a calmer way to be. You don't know me any other way and I can't help but harvest a small amount of curiosity verging on jealousy to know what it must be like knowing me first and then BPD.

I wonder and then a small smile grows with the realisation you are not alone...

My Personal Take on Borderline Personality Disorder

Kevin Healy

I work as Clinical Director of the Cassel Hospital Therapeutic Community. We have three clinical services working with children and families, with young people and with adults, all of whom suffer the impact of disordered personality functioning. Our patients live with and learn to face a lot of pain, distress and disturbance affecting themselves, their family members and friends, and their professional networks.

Diagnostic systems, to my way of thinking, are man made abstractions justifiable only if they are useful. A diagnosis of personality disorder, or more particularly of borderline personality disorder, is only useful if it leads to appropriate engagement and intervention for the individual with the diagnosis. Engagement and intervention may be appropriate if current healthy functioning is supported, and current unhealthy functioning is challenged and changed. I do not believe that a diagnosis of personality disorder currently leads to the provision of appropriate engagement and intervention. Rather, I believe it often continues to be 'a diagnosis of exclusion'.

All of us as individuals come together to form communities in society, which we organise and structure in ways that we hope bring maximum benefit to maximum numbers of people. Those who are diagnosed as severely mentally ill suffering from schizophrenia, or manic depressive psychosis or severe depression, can sometimes serve as a receptacle for mental distress for those others in society who do not judge themselves to be mentally ill. Many individuals find it very uncomfortable to be in touch with their own sadness, despair, disordered thinking patterns and madness. It is easier to feel such states are lodged in others who are clearly different and clearly less fortunate than us. Those with personality disorder, whose behaviours are akin to the behaviours associated with ordinary living and whose thought processes and emotions may represent more extreme forms of ordinary human functioning, are clearly not so different. It may be that members of communities and of society need more actively to exclude such individuals so as to create a difference in order to maintain the notion that mental distress is something other individuals feel, and not ourselves.

I am not sure why I have come to work in this area. I recall as a teenager deciding to study medicine so that I could work as a psychiatrist, so that I could train in psychotherapy. I didn't know what I was really getting into when I set out. I did not know then, nor do I fully know now, the personal psychological issues that drew me to this line of work. I am basically a nice bloke, usually not prone to extremes. I have been depressed and off work for two periods during my professional life. Perhaps I am drawn to work with issues in other individuals that I also seek to address in myself. Whatever the reason that underlines my attraction to this way of working, grasping chance opportunities as they present, alongside persistence and resilience in following through my interests have led me to where I am now.

In my current role I see individuals, whether patients or staff, struggle with a range of human emotions and human behaviours. I see the courage involved in all concerned in beginning to take the risks involved in changing. I see individuals, whether patients or staff, getting on with their lives and finding a creativity in themselves whether around family life or professional achievements. I make very real contacts with individuals, which are humbling, empowering and motivating. I therefore continue to do this work.

Untitled
Mark Oliver

In my experience as a staff nurse working in the areas of acute admissions and psychiatric intensive care (areas where patients with BPD are commonly admitted), I've noticed there are areas of common concern that I find myself talking about very often. Here are two of them:

"Why do I do what I do?"
Well, the answer to this will be different for everyone, but I can offer a little bit of insight – *you do it because it works.* We're all just trying to get along in this world and we've all found ways of coping with stress. At some point in your life you found that harming yourself helped to relieve the pain and stress you feel inside. It wasn't a long-term solution and the pain and stress came back,

but it helped a bit – it worked for a while. Humans are funny, we'll keep doing things that help in the short-term even if we know that it's bad for us in the long-term. It's the same reason why people keep smoking, even though they know they should quit. And just like smoking, we can become addicted to behaviours. So when you first harmed yourself, the fact that it worked for a little while made it all the more likely that you'd do it again and again and again. It doesn't take long for it to become a habit, and habits are difficult to break if they're helping you to feel better. Sometimes habits get out of hand and begin to make it difficult to just get on with life – self-harming can be like that. What used to help starts to become a hindrance. Recognizing that you do what you do because it works is the first step to 1) not being so hard on yourself, and 2) breaking the habit.

"Am I going to be like this forever?"
Here's an interesting fact- *you don't tend to see BPD in elderly wards.* Maybe the odd case here and there, but I've never seen it. Something has happened to people with BPD that means they're not requiring hospitalization at the age of 60+. One solution is that people with BPD don't reach that age (not an unreasonable suggestion considering the amount of suicidal/self-harming behaviour associated with BPD). And yet looking at the figures suggests that the suicide rate of BPD is 10%. This is high, but no higher than something like schizophrenia, and sadly the number of elderly people with schizophrenia is very high. No, something else has happened to explain why people in their 60s are no longer requiring hospital treatment for BPD. I like to think that they reached a stage in their lives where they found another way

of coping with pain and stress than by being self-destructive. I have had the pleasure of seeing many ex-patients come on to the ward after a gap of a couple of years, looking brighter and more alive, sometimes showing off the skin-grafts to their arms that have covered the years' worth of scar tissue. If they can break the cycle you can too.

How to break the cycle? That differs from person to person. A few general points might help though. Firstly, by recognising that there is a reason why you do what you do, you have made the first step towards changing it. Secondly, don't expect to change overnight, it probably took several years to get where you are now – be realistic about how long it'll take to change your ways of coping. Thirdly, give yourself a break – if certain situations are likely to make things worse, don't put yourself through them. You have the power to make good or bad decisions about your life... Things can seem suddenly very different if you start to make decisions that don't end up in confrontation, trouble, or just more stress. Fourthly, try to find a therapist you can trust.

Good luck. I know it's not easy. Just remember there are no quick fixes, but things **can** get better.

The Trouble With Boundaries
Ashman

You can't say that - it's emotional blackmail.
You can't do that - it's completely unfair.
You can't expect, and you're too demanding,
But remember we love you,
And we know that we care.

Untitled
D. Lines

I was first "diagnosed" as a Carer in 1990. I had not been feeling ill prior to the diagnosis and consequently it came as a complete surprise to me. At the time, I was talking to our family GP about my son who had been diagnosed as BPD. His diagnosis was subsequently "upgraded" to APD and then again on another occasion, to PPD by various Mental Health Professionals. Clearly, someone was being "diagnostically challenged". Anyway, unprompted by me, (I had gone to see him on another matter) the GP decided to "explain" to me, why my 20 year old son had a tendency to self-harm. "They do it to get attention Mr Lines" he declared. Now, I really did not know who the "they" were, but there was one thing I did know. My son who was also HIV positive, had always told me that he cut himself because it seemed the only way he could distract himself from some very torturous thoughts. He never wanted attention for these cuts and often hid them from everyone. I considered my son to be an honest person and his explanation seemed much more plausible to me than the GP's "professional" opinion. Our GP did not appreciate his opinion being challenged, nor was he comfortable when I then chose to remind him that my son also had a right to complete confidentiality in all medical matters. I knew that he would certainly not appreciate his rights being discarded. "Some Carer's just can't accept the truth!" was the exasperated retort I got from the GP. I remember he spat out the word "Carer" loudly and quickly. Try that for yourself. Say the word fast, and it sounds like an untreatable nervous cough. I don't believe it's contagious though – but then again, I would say that, wouldn't I?

Since the original diagnosis, I have learnt much about "my condition". Did you know that according to some "Mental Health professionals", there are two strains of the Carer disease? There is the very treatable "Good Carer syndrome" and also the irksome and untreatable, "Bad Carer syndrome". The former is welcomed with open arms by them, but the latter is avoided like the plague by them whenever possible.   Apparently though, both strains are quickly identifiable.

Some "Good Carers" are easy to spot and are a joy to behold. They sit quietly, totally in awe of the MH Professional confronting them and although probably not understanding a word that is being spoken, they are much too polite to ask questions. They accept without question everything they hear – even if not for the first time, what they hear blatantly contradicts something that they had previously been told by another MH professional. They are easily convinced that every MH professional always knows best and they have the strength of character to ensure that the person they care for "understands" that fact - even if they protest otherwise. The "Good Carer" instinctively knows that verbal defiance of any psychotherapy practices is tantamount to blasphemy. "Good Carers" often discuss their personal dilemmas with their sympathetic local milkman. He is often a source of much wisdom, because he also speaks with Mrs Jones who lives at 11 Sesame St - and who also has similar dilemmas with her Alzheimer's-afflicted mother. "Good Carers" are sometimes regarded as martyrs by their sympathetic friends and consequently, they often evolve to regard themselves as such.

"Bad Carers" are regarded by some MH professionals as an absolute pain in the backside. Believe it or not, these Carers are often completely incapable of comprehending the absolute infallibility of PD "treatment plans". Although most reasonable people readily accept that some MH Professionals must employ the tactics similar to the Grand old Duke of York, the "Bad Carers" have the audacity to question why anyone should have to march up and down the same old hill. Foolishly, they actually believe that there is some rationality behind the thinking of the person they care for. If that person strongly objects to marching up and down the same old hill the "Bad Carer" is inclined to agree with them. They also have a ridiculous tendency to praise the people they care for when minor goals are achieved, instead of looking at the "bigger picture" and focusing on what has not yet been possible. Unlike the "Good Carers", the "Bad Carers" have yet to learn that compassion is an obstacle to "progress". The "Good Carers" have long since learnt that indifference is the key to "success". I have sometimes managed to console

176

myself by imagining that inside every "Good Carer" there is a "Bad Carer" trying to get out. I know this is only a figment of my imagination, but how else can "Bad Carers" like me manage to live with themselves?

Suicide – No More Goodbyes?
Anonymous

I used to think that suicide was something other people had to deal with. I was completely naive about the feelings that this act could engender when the person you love tries to end their own life. In the past 6 years I have experienced three unsuccessful suicide attempts by my wife, each one progressively becoming more desperate and carefully planned.

I have experienced four distinct emotional stages as a result of my wife's failed suicide attempts. I hope that by writing about my experiences, it may provide an insight into the crippling emotions that follow this destructive act.

1) Survival mode (adrenalin driven)

> This is when you are confronted with the danger of the situation. It is such a shock that your mind protects you from the reality of what is happening in front of you. You switch off your emotions to get on with the mechanics of life saving. In this stage you are responsible, you have been forced to hold this person's life in your hands. This

adrenalin driven state makes you think clearly and enables you to get help.

2) Disbelief (dream like state)

This stage comes about when you have time to reflect on the enormity of the situation that you find yourself in. It starts when the blues and twos and A&E departments are gone. You find yourself in intensive care, watching your loved ones heart trace. It's quiet and you feel so alone. The ward staff encourage you to take regular breaks from sitting by the bed, so you walk around the long empty hospital corridors searching for answers.

You hide yourself away, you cannot cope with talking to people as you need to think. You find a quiet isolated spot and start to cry. The release makes you feel a little stronger, you use this strength to reflect on the reasons why your loved one wanted to take their own life. Whilst you wait, praying for your loved one to wake up and be ok, you feel as though this is happening to someone else - like you're an actor in a movie. This is probably because your mind can not accept the situation you find yourself in. I suppose it's another defence mechanism to remove you from the pain of facing up to the situation straight away.

3) Realisation (the world collapses)

This stage comes when the person you love starts to wake up. You are cautiously relieved, however your mind turns to worrying if your loved one has any lasting medical conditions as a result of (in my case) the medication passing through her system. Could she be brain damaged, paralysed or even not recognise me? Whilst you worry about whether physical danger has passed, the next stage you are completely unprepared for. It hits you so hard, much harder than what you have just experienced over the past 24 hours.

Your loved one realises that they are in fact alive, and they are angry with you for saving their life. This is the most distressing thing about the whole situation. You have given your all, been to hell and back and in some way, you want your loved one to say they didn't intend to take it this far and now they are shocked by what they have done and thus want to live. But nothing of the sort! Their true feelings surface and you are forced to face up to the fact that this despair, the emotion that very nearly killed your loved one, has still got a grip and will not let go!

4) Reflection (high anxiety lifestyle)

Your loved one had probably been hiding their intentions from you in the weeks prior to the suicide attempt. You were getting on with your life, not really understanding the depth of despair that your loved one was experiencing. They had told you that they couldn't cope but you brushed this off as you didn't understand the true extent of their pain. You now feel immensely guilty for disbelieving them or for keeping your head down to focus on your own life.

When you eventually find the time to reflect on the events that lead up to the actual suicide attempt, you spot signs that were shouting at you "HELP"! However hard your loved one tried to hide their despair, there were subtle signs that you should have looked out for and responded to.

This reflective process makes you hyper-vigilant, which eventually becomes a way of life for you. You will not drop your guard as you had done before and consequently you live in a high state of anxiety.

These experiences and very strong emotions have changed me forever. I feel that I have a better understanding of the emotional pain that my wife feels and the true extent of despair in its strongest most destructive form.

I hope by me writing this article, you have gained some understanding of the devastating effects of potentially losing someone you love to suicide.

In Memoriam
Gail Silver

Words are such small comfort,
They'll never truly say
How full of sorrow is my heart
That Sue has passed away.
Her death should be a blessing
But it doesn't ease the pain;
To know she no more suffers
Nor ever will again.

We doubt this everlasting ache
Will ever pass with time
Or these softly flowing tears
Will cease: Our spirits climb.
We are selfish with our feelings.
We can't let our loved ones go.
We will not let ourselves believe
That God has made death so.
We want them back!
How dare they steal away!
Why did the one that we so loved
Break our heart this way?

But then this anger leaves us.
Our pain begins to fade.
Our memories take the place of it
And quiet thoughts pervade.
In the stillness of the evening
When all is peace and calm,
The times when we were happiest
Creep in ~ a quiet balm.
It's then that grieving passes,
But there may be gentle sorrow.
We'll get on with our lives now

And look towards tomorrow.

Though now you're feeling desolate;
Alone, perhaps afraid,
Remember through this tunnel
Is a green and pleasant glade.
Whatever you are feeling
Be assured you're not alone.
Someone's thoughts are with you:
They're no further than the phone.

And then, there comes the sunshine
Where only rain did fall.
We're at peace within ourselves
And walk both straight and tall!

5. Resources

Useful Organisations and Websites

Contact details and helpline times correct at time of publication.

Association of Therapeutic Communities
Barns Centre
Church Lane
Toddington, near Cheltenham,
Gloucestshire
GL54 5DQ
telephone: 01242 620077
email: post@therapeuticcommunities.org
website: www.therapeuticcommunities.org

Association to Assist Persons with Emotional Lesions (AAPEL)
http://www.aapel.org/index_us

Beyond Abuse
email: leigh@beyondabuse.org
website: www.beyondabuse.org

Borderline Personality Information
http://www.borderlinepersonality.info

Borderline UK
PO Box 77
Workington
Cumbria
CA14 9AA
email: info@borderlineuk.co.uk
website: www.borderlineuk.co.uk

Yahoo group:
http://groups.yahoo.com/group/borderlineuk

BPD Carers
Yahoo group:
http://groups.yahoo.com/group/bpdcarers

BPD World
4 King Street
Wakefield
WF1 2SQ
telephone: 08700 887053
email: info@bpdworld.org
website: www.bpdworld.org

Bristol Crisis Service for Women
PO Box 654
Bristol
BS99 1XH
administrative enquiries: 0117 927 9600
helpline: 0117 925 1119 (Fri/Sat 9pm – 12:30 am;
Sun 6-9pm)
email: bcsw@btconnect.com
website: www.users.zetnet.co.uk/bcsw

Eating Disorders Association
103 Prince of Wales Road
Norwich
NR1 1DW
helpline: 0845 634 1414 (Mon-Fri: 8:30am-8:30pm;
Sat: 1-4:30pm)
email: info@edauk.com
helpline email: helpmail@edauk.com
website: www.edauk.com

First Steps to Freedom
1 Taylor Close
Kenilworth
Warwickshire
CV8 2LW
administrative enquiries: 01926 864473
helpline: 0845 120 2916 (10 am - 10 pm)
email: firststeps@btconnect.com
website: www.first-steps.org

Helen's World of BPD Resources
http://www.bpdresources.com/index.html

James Nayler Foundation
PO Box 49
Ventnor
PO38 9AA
telephone: 01983 401 700
email: info@truthtrustconsent.com
website: www.truthtrustconsent.com

MadNOTBad
c/o The Marlene Reid Centre
85 Belvoir Road
Coalville
Leicestershire
LE67 3PH
email: rachel@madnotbad.co.uk
website: www.madnotbad.co.uk

MIND
15-19 Broadway
London
E15 4BQ
administrative enquiries: 020 8519 2122
information line: 0845 766 0163
email: contact@mind.org.uk
website: www.mind.org.uk

National Institute for Mental Health in England (NIMHE)
Room 8E
46 Quarry House
Quarry Hill
Leeds
LS2 7UE
Telephone: 0113 2545127
Email: ask@nihme.org.uk
Website: www.nimhe.org.uk

National Self Harm Network
PO Box 7264
Nottingham
NG1 6WJ
email: info@nshn.co.uk
website: www.nshn.co.uk

Recover Your Life
www.recoveryourlife.com

Samaritans
helpline: 08457 909090 (24 hour)
email: jo@samaritans.org
website: www.samaritans.org

SANE
1st Floor Cityside House
40 Adler Street
London
E1 1EE
administrative enquiries: 020 7375 2001
helpline: 0845 767 8000 (weekdays: noon–11pm;
weekends: noon-6pm)
email: info@saneline.org.uk
website: www.sane.org.uk

Self Injury UK
website: www.siuk.org
Yahoo group: http://groups.yahoo.com/group/siuk

Further Reading

This is not a comprehensive list. Additional information may be found from the organisations and websites listed above.

Bell, L. 2003. *Managing Intense Emotions and Overcoming Self-Destructive Habits: A Self-Help Manual* Brunner-Routledge. (ISBN 1583919155)

Bockian, N., Porr, V. and N. Villagran. 2002. *New Hope For People With Borderline Personality Disorder* Crown Publications. (ISBN 0-7615-2572-6)

Freeman, A. and G. M. Fusco. 2003. *Borderline Personality Disorder: A Therapist's Guide to Taking Control* W.W. Norton & Company Ltd. (ISBN: 0393703525)

Fusco, G. M. and A. Freeman. 2003. *Borderline Personality Disorder: A Patient's Guide to Taking Control* W.W. Norton & Company Ltd. (ISBN: 0393703533)

Gunderson, J. G. 2001. *Borderline Personality Disorder: A Clinical Guide.* American Psychiatric Publishing Inc. (ISBN: 1585620165)

Lineham, M. 1993. *Cognitive Behavioural Treatment of Borderline Personality Disorder* Guilford Press. (ISBN: 0898621836)

Lineham, M. 1993. *Skills Training Manual for Treating Borderline Personality Disorder (Diagnosis*

& *Treatment of Mental Disorders)* Guilford Press.
(ISBN: 0898620341)

Mason, P. and R. Kreger. 1998. *Stop Walking on
Eggshells: Coping When Someone You Care About
Has Borderline Personality Disorder* New
Harbinger Publications. (ISBN 157224108X)

Mind. 2004. *Understanding Borderline Personality
Disorder.* Mind Publications.
(ISBN 1-903567-19-X)

Reiland, R. 2004. *Get Me Out of Here: My
Recovery from Borderline Personality Disorder*
Information & Educational Services. (ISBN:
1592850995)

Spradlin, S.E. 2003. *Don't Let Your Emotions Run
Your Life.* New Harbinger Publications. (ISBN
1572243090)

Policy Documentation

National Institute for Mental Health in England.
2003. *Breaking the Cycle of Rejection The
Personality Disorder Capabilities Framework.*
(www.nimhe.org.uk/downloads/personalitydisorders
.pdf)

National Institute for Mental Health in England.
2003. *Personality Disorder: No Longer a diagnosis
of exclusion.*
(http://www.dh.gov.uk/assetRoot/04/05/42/30/0405
4230.pdf)

Diagnostic Criteria

DSM-IV diagnostic criteria for Borderline Personality Disorder

The 4th edition of the Diagnostic and Statistical Manual of mental disorders (DSM-IV) is the most recent classification of mental illnesses produced by the American Psychiatric Association. It is used primarily in the USA for diagnosing mental health problems. A diagnosis of Borderline Personality Disorder requires that *at least five* of the following nine criteria are met:

1) Frantic efforts to avoid real or imagined abandonment. **Note:** Does not include suicidal or self-mutilating behaviour, which is covered in criterion 5.

2) A pattern of unstable and intense interpersonal relationships characterised by alternating between extremes of idealization and devaluation

3) Identity disturbance: markedly and persistently unstable self-image or sense of self

4) Impulsivity in at least two areas that are potentially self-damaging (e.g., spending, sex, substance abuse, reckless driving, binge eating). **Note:** Does not include suicidal or self-mutilating behaviour, which is covered in criterion 5.

5) Recurrent suicidal behaviour, gestures, or threats, or self-mutilating behaviour

6) Affective instability due to a marked reactivity of mood (e.g., intense episodic dysphoria, irritability, or anxiety usually lasting a few hours and only rarely more than a few days)

7) Chronic feelings of emptiness

8) Inappropriate, intense anger or difficulty controlling anger (e.g., frequent displays of temper, constant anger, recurrent physical fights)

9) Transient stress-related paranoid ideation or severe dissociative symptoms

In addition, the symptoms must have been present from at least adolescence and they must interfere significantly with functioning at work, home, and/or in interpersonal relationships. The difficulties must not be better explained by the presence of another mental illness, a general medical condition, or the effects of a substance.

Reprinted with permission from the Diagnostic and Statistical Manual of Mental Disorders Fourth Edition, Text Revision, (Copyright 2000). American Psychiatric Association.

ICD-10 diagnostic criteria for Emotionally Unstable Personality Disorder, Borderline Type

The International Classification of Diseases is produced by the World Health Organisation and is currently in its tenth edition (ICD-10). It is used more commonly in Europe. The diagnostic criteria are broadly similar to those in the DSM-IV, however the disorder has a different name and is treated as a sub-classification of Emotionally Unstable Personality Disorder. Below is the description of and diagnostic criteria for Emotionally Unstable Personality Disorder and its two diagnostic sub-classifications – impulsive type and borderline type.

Emotionally unstable personality disorder

A personality disorder characterized by a definite tendency to act impulsively and without consideration of the consequences; the mood is unpredictable and capricious. There is a liability to outbursts of emotion and an incapacity to control the behavioural explosions. There is a tendency to quarrelsome behaviour and to conflicts with others, especially when impulsive acts are thwarted or censored. Two types may be distinguished: the impulsive type, characterized predominantly by emotional instability and lack of impulse control, and the borderline type, characterized in addition by disturbances in self-image, aims, and internal preferences, by chronic feelings of emptiness, by intense and unstable interpersonal relationships, and by a tendency to self-destructive behaviour, including suicide gestures and attempts.

Impulsive type

The predominant characteristics are emotional instability and lack of impulse control. Outbursts of violence or threatening behaviour are common, particularly in response to criticism by others. At least three of the following criteria must be met, one of which must be criterion 2:

1) Marked tendency to act unexpectedly and without consideration of the consequences

2) Marked tendency to quarrelsome behaviour and to conflicts with others, especially when impulsive acts are thwarted or criticised

3) Liability to outbursts of anger or violence, with inability to control the resulting behavioural explosions

4) Difficult in maintaining any course or action that offers no immediate reward

5) Unstable and capricious mood

Borderline type
Several of the characteristics of emotional instability are present; in addition, the patient's own self-image, aims, and internal preferences (including sexual) are often unclear or disturbed. There are usually chronic feelings of emptiness. A liability to become involved in intense and unstable relationships may cause repeated emotional crises and may be associated with excessive efforts to avoid abandonment and a series of suicidal threats or acts or self-harm (although these may occur without obvious precipitants). For a diagnosis, at least three of the above five criteria for impulsive type must be met, as well as at least two of the following five criteria:

1) Disturbances in and uncertainty about self-image, aims, and internal preferences (including sexual)

2) Liability to become involved in intense and unstable relationships, often leading to emotional crises

3) Excessive efforts to avoid abandonment

4) Recurrent threats or acts of self harm

5) Chronic feelings of emptiness

International Statistical Classification of Diseases and Health Related Problems (The) ICD-10. 1990. World Health Organisation

Printed in the United Kingdom
by Lightning Source UK Ltd.
113876UKS00001B/194